THE VEGAN GUIDE

*Everything you need to embrace
the world's fastest growing way of life*

Welcome to veganism – the kindest, healthiest and tastiest way of living.

This ground-breaking book covers:

- An amazing range of vegan food from around the world.
- Essential cooking techniques.
- Replacing animal products in your favourite dishes.
- Shopping and eating out.
- The twenty tribes of vegan.
- How veganism can save your life - and many others.
- What to say to friends and relatives.

With this guide, you'll be able to become vegan and have a great time doing it. As well as cooking, there's a comprehensive guide to where vegans get protein, calcium, omegas and all the essential nutrients.

For those on a tight budget, we reveal secrets of eating vegan for little more than £1 a day.

Also covered are vegan alcohol, shoes, clothing, cosmetics, holidays, pet food, and raising vegan children.

Whether you're into baking or raw foods, wholefoods or fast food, eco-activism or the high life, this is the complete handbook for all vegans, from total beginner to those ready to spread the word.

THE VEGAN GUIDE – everything you need
to embrace the world's fastest growing way of life

1st edition by Alex Bourke & Ronny Worsey

ISBN 978-1-902259-22-2 paperback
ISBN 978-1-902259-21-5 kindle

Published January 2021
by Vegan Guides Ltd
2 Hilborough Court, Livermere Road, London E8 4LG, UK

Distributed in UK by Gardners
Gardners.com

TheVeganGuide.info
VeganGuides.uk

Printed by Buxton Press, England

THE VEGAN GUIDE

*Everything you need to embrace
the world's fastest growing way of life*

by

Alex Bourke & Ronny Worsey

with

Scarlet Hughes, nutritionist
Chrissy Leyland, mother, chef & counsellor
Dr Mike Hooper, GP & nutritionist
Prof Andrew Knight, vet
Dean Bracher, campaigner
Rudy Penando, founder of Pogo Cafe, VX and SSOV

Consultants
Catherine Laurence BA, MSc
Sandra Hood, dietitian
Dr Shireen Kassam
Julia Wilde

TheVeganGuide.info

Also by Alex Bourke & Ronny Worsey
Vegetarian North of England
Vegetarian Scotland
Campaign Against Cruelty – an activist's handbook

By Alex Bourke
The Hippy Cookbook
The Vegan Guide to Paris
The Cruelty-Free Guide to London (with Paul Gaynor)
Vegetarian London (with Paul Gaynor)
Vegetarian London 3rd ed. (with Paul Gaynor)
Vegetarian London 4th ed. (with Jennifer Wharton)
Vegetarian London 2005
Vegetarian London 2008
Vegetarian Britain (with Alan Todd)
Vegetarian Britain 2nd ed. (with Katrina Holland)
Vegetarian Britain 2006
Vegetarian France (with Laurence Auger & Jean-Luc Ferrante)
Vegetarian Europe
Vegetarian East of England
Vegetarian Central London
Vegan Central London
Vegan East London
Vegan North London
Vegan South London
Vegan West London
Vegan London Complete

Animal Rights – a universal declaration (film, with Harry Snell)

By Ronny Worsey
The Cake Scoffer
The Breakfast Scoffer
Return of the Cake Scoffer
The Salad Scofl Rights

By Andrew Knight
The Costs and Benefits of Animal Experiments

"Veganism is a way of living which seeks to exclude, as far as is possible and practicable, all forms of exploitation of, and cruelty to, animals for food, clothing or any other purpose."

The Vegan Society

Contents

4 Vegan Tribes 79

- Animal Activists
- Animal Rescuers
- Baketivists
- Convenience Food Fans
- Eco-Activists
- Fitness Junkies
- Foodies
- Food Not Bombs and People's Kitchen
- Foragers
- Gleegans
- Guru Followers
- Health Enthusiasts
- Macrobiotics
- Plant-based People
- Pretenders
- Raw Fooders
- Religious Practitioners
- Spiritual Seekers of Truth
- Skinny Bitches
- Straight Edgers
- Suspicious Minds
- Trolls
- Veeks

5 Beyond Food

Vegan Shoes and Clothing 95
Household Products and Cosmetics 97
Alcoholic Drinks 98
Vegan Pet Food 101

6 Family and Friends

Being Vegan in a pre-Vegan World 107

- Level 1 Vegan – state your food needs, without justifying
- Level 2 Vegan – answer questions
- Level 3 Vegan – defend against attacks
- Level 4 Vegan – teacher
- Level 5 Vegan – instructor trainer
- Ethical veganism is a protected belief

Vegan Parenting 114

CHAPTER 1

The Vegans Are Coming

YOU ARE POWERFUL

You can help to create the compassionate, healthy, sustainable world that you want to live in.

By deciding to go vegan, you transform your inner world and send positive ripples outwards. Veganism is not simply a diet, or a lifestyle choice. It is a powerful and positive change in how we think, that is gaining momentum around the world.

This book shows you how to go, be and stay vegan. We explain all the practicalities of shopping, cooking and eating out on any budget, as well as arming you with all the knowledge you need about nutrition. We also cover the powerful ethical and environmental arguments against livestock farming.

With your black belt in veganism, you will know how to defend yourself in any situation. You will be able to explain your choices calmly and clearly so that others understand, and bat away any unhelpful assumptions and stereotypes. A vegan warrior wants to help others to realise their full potential.

We have been black belt vegans for decades, doing and teaching veganism. We have worked in restaurant kitchens and bakeries, and written cookbooks and vegan travel guides. We have also worked in national vegan organisations such as Animal Aid, Viva! and The Vegan Society, and collaborated with and learned from the most effective and successful vegan activists and teachers around the world. We have run workshops, and given local and national radio and television interviews. In this book we will teach you to handle situations with confidence, knowledge, and in a way that will inspire others to join us.

GETTING STARTED

Going vegan starts by declaring yourself to be vegan.

1. *Plan the veganisation of your favourite meals and snacks* – Some will already be vegan, and others can easily be adapted. Go to chapter 3: How to Eat Vegan.

2. *Stock your kitchen* – Mealtimes become easy if you stock up with store cupboard basics.

3. *No time to cook?* – Get in some ready made foods, and meat and cheese replacers.

4. *Be ready for eating out* – Investigate local cafes, restaurants and shops. And *load up on treats* for snacking and boosting your energy during a busy day.

5. *Know your nutrients* – Arm yourself with the facts. Go to chapter 2: A Balanced Diet.

6. *Get some vegan buddies* – It's great to have a tribe to share with. Read chapter 4: Vegan Tribes.

7. *If you have a problem, if no one else can help* – Call in the V-Team to support you. There are many long-established charities and campaigning groups who publish magazines, leaflets, fact sheets and websites, plus hundreds of Facebook vegan discussion groups, probably including at least one covering your local area. Check out chapter 8: The Way of the Vegan.

Thank you for going vegan – have fun and good luck!

VEGAN FOOD AROUND THE WORLD

What do vegans eat?

Vegans eat thousands of foods from hundreds of countries. Here are some favourites.

Spanish *tapas:* patatas bravas, toasted almonds, olives, garlic mushrooms, lentil or chickpea casserole, gazpacho soup, sparagus and artichoke salad.

Brazilian feijoada with black beans with vegan sausage and/or veg.

Strawberry coconut-based **cheesecake**.

Spanish tapas   Brazilian feijoada   Strawberry cheesecake

Thai tofu curry

British phish & chips

Seitan steak

Chinese buffet

Indian thali

Ethiopian injera feast

South Indian dosa

Raw food buffet

Indonesian tempeh kebab

Thai green, red or yellow tofu **curry** with steamed sticky rice.

Banana blossom **phish and chips**.

Seitan steak with sweet potato fries, loaded with vegan cheese and roasted veg. Seitan is a high-protein meat replacer made from wheat gluten.

Chinese buffet including mock duck, seitan black pepper "pork", egg-free noodles, stir-fry veg, black mushrooms, pak choi, red and yellow pepper stir-fry.

Indian thali with samosa, onion bhajia, aloo gobi (spicy potato), brinjal (aubergine), chana masala (chickpeas), lentil dal soup, popadoms and naan bread.

Ethiopian injera flatbread with lentil dishes and salads.

South Indian crispy **dosa** pancake filled with veg, with uttapam lentil pizza and chutneys.

Raw superfood **salads.**

Indonesian tempeh kebab with satay sauce. Tempeh is a traditional meat replacer made from fermented soya beans.

Moroccan chickpea and apricot **tagine** stew with couscous.

Soya, seitan, bean, mycoprotein or
mushroom-based **burger with wedges**.

Japanese bento boxes with fake fish sushi, rice and veg maki rolls,
tempura deep fried veg, crispy seaweed, noodles.

Cashew nut **roast** with Yorkshire pudding, veggies,
new potatoes and onion gravy.

British cooked breakfast with vegan sausages and scrambled tofu.

Italian vegan ham, chorizo and mozzarella **pizza**.

Mexican black bean **burrito** with guacamole, jalapenos and chili sauce.

Middle Eastern falafel in pitta with hummus,
salad, pepper, tahini sesame sauce.

Caribbean platter with chickpea curry, pumpkin curry, lentil stew,
ackee, callaloo, plantain, fried dumplings, seaweed fritters, salad.

North African tagine

Burger with wedges

Japanese bento boxes

Sunday roast dinner

British cooked breakfast

Italian "meaty" pizza

Mexican burrito

Middle Eastern falafel

Caribbean platter

Chick'n wingz

Smoothie bowl

Sausage rolls

Chocolate ice cream

Ice cream pancake

Protein shake

Cake

Muffins and brownies

Cupcakes

Chick'n wingz made from seitan in barbecue sauce.

Smoothie bowl with granola, nuts, seeds and fruit.

Soya sausage rolls.

Vanilla, chocolate or strawberry soya or coconut **ice cream.**

Warm **pancake** filled with ice cream and served
with chocolate and vanilla soya dessert.

Almond **milkshake** with protein powder (soya, pea or hemp),
banana, spirulina and ground flax seeds.

Egg and dairy-free cakes such as blueberry and almond cake.

Chocolate **brownies and** blueberry **muffins.**

Cupcakes.

Chocolate bars

Chocolate truffles

Energy balls

Plant milks

Vegan cheese

Vegan yogurt

Vegan wine

Vegan beer

Vegan honey

Vegans around the world create foods and dishes using ingredients from the following groups of foods:

Grains: Amaranth, barley, buckwheat, bulgur, cassava, kamut, millet, oats, quinoa, rice, rye, sorghum, spelt, teff, triticale, wheat.

Pulses, these are lentils and beans, which are also called legumes in some countries: Aduki, black, blackeye, borlotti, broad, butter, cannellini, chickpea (garbanzo, gram), flageolet, lentils (black, brown, green, puy, red, yellow), haricot, kidney, lima, lupin, mung, pinto, split peas, soya.

Vegetables: Ackee, artichoke, asparagus, aubergine (eggplant), beetroot, broccoli, Brussels sprout, cabbage, callaloo, carrot, cauliflower, celeriac, celery, chard, chicory, courgette (zucchini), cucumber, daikon, endive, fennel, garlic, ginger, kale, kohlrabi, leeks, lettuce, marrow, mooli, mushroom, nettle, okra, onion, pak choi, parsnip, pea, pepper, plantain, potato, pumpkin, radish, runner bean, seaweed, sorrell, spinach, spring onion, squash, swede, sweetcorn (maize), sweet potato, tomato, turnip, yam, watercress.

Fruits: Apple, apricot, avocado, banana, blackberry, blackcurrant, blueberry, breadfruit, cherry, clementine, coconut, cranberry, custard apple, date, durian, elderberry, fig, goji berry, gooseberry, grapes, grapefruit, guava, jackfruit, kiwi fruit, kumquat, lemon, lime, lychee, mandarin, mango, melons, mulberry, nectarine, olive, orange, papaya, passionfruit, peach, pear, persimmon (kaki), pineapple, plum/prune, pomegranate, quince, raspberry, rambutan, redcurrant, satsuma, star fruit, strawberry, tangerine, watermelon, whitecurrant.

Nuts: Almond, Brazil, cashew, chestnut, hazelnut, macadamia, peanut*, pecan, pistachio, walnut. (*Peanuts are botanically a pulse, not a fruit or nut, as they grow in pods underground.)

Seeds: chia, flax (linseed), hemp, pine nut, poppy, pumpkin, sesame, sunflower.

Modern vegan cuisine is a synthesis of the healthiest foods and fun foods from all over the world. Take your choice from the world's thousands of edible plants and everything made from them.

WHY VEGAN

Whether you are taking the first steps on the path to going vegan or
have completely done so already, you may be tempted to skip this
section. You are bound to get questions from friends, family and
co-workers about why you've done it. Here are some things you can say.

What's wrong with eating animals?

Animals: Most farmed animals never see daylight or fresh air, and are
killed at a tiny fraction of their natural lifespan. They are bred for the
sole purpose of being units of food production. They don't have names.
They don't have the chance to explore, play, interact naturally and
express their instincts. Free range and organically farmed animals
have a little more space, though are killed just as violently.

Health: Meat eaters suffer much more from obesity, heart disease,
high blood pressure, diabetes type 2, cancer and constipation.

Animal foods are responsible for almost all food poisoning,
including E. coli, salmonella, listeria and campylobacter.

Antibiotic resistant bacteria such as MRSA result from the overuse of
antibiotics. 75% of all antibiotics in Europe and America are given to
intensively farmed animals and fish, not just to prevent disease, but
also as growth promoters. Antibiotic and disinfectant resistant bacteria
such as E. coli develop, then infect farm workers, and enter the
human food supply, for example via pig meat in supermarkets.
The emergence of bacteria resistant to most or all antibiotics
is one of the greatest threats of our time.

Pandemics: COVID-19 was not the first disease to jump from animals that we eat to humans. So did vCJD (mad cow disease), swine and bird flu, HIV/AIDS (chimps), ebola (bats or primates), and at least 60% of new infectious diseases. The SARS coronavirus in 2002-4 killed one in ten people infected, with 55% of those aged over 60. Ebola, which is not airborne, kills around 50% of those infected. Many scientists believe that "the big one", an airborne pandemic with a fatality rate comparable to ebola, could cross over from animals into humans this century. If, that is, we continue to eat animals. Pandemics love factory farms, animal markets and meat processing centres.

Environment: Most deforestation is for cattle or growing soya for animal feed. Livestock farming is the biggest source of water pollution. It takes far more land, water, fuel and electricity to farm animals than to farm plants.

Given all the above, we believe that eating animals is unjustified and should be consigned to the dustbin of history.

Now, what's so great about being vegan?

Animals: Animals are people in different bodies, as anyone who lives with a dog or cat knows. Like us they feel affection, joy, happiness, and they love to play. They also feel sadness, fear, pain and suffering. Do we really need to say any more?

Health: Certain vegan diets can stop the progression of and even reverse most heart disease and reverse all diabetes type 2 within weeks, without drugs or surgery. Being vegan massively reduces your chances of getting heart disease in the first place, and when done correctly makes diabetes type 2 impossible. You can read about this in chapter 7.

Pandemics: No factory farming, no hunting, no animals in markets, will mean no zoonotic diseases crossing over from wild animals to decimate us or bring our economies to a standstill for a year. With the world's population heading towards 9 billion, mostly crowded together in cities, veganism is our best chance of avoiding new coronavirus pandemics and worse.

Environment: Vegans use less than half as much land as non-vegans to grow our food, some say as little as 20%. That will free up land for re-wilding, putting back billions of trees, returning the prisoners in zoos to their natural habitats, soaking up carbon dioxide, and saving the planet for the thousands of generations who will come after us.

Taste: Vegan food is a gorgeous fusion of the best foods from around the world.

Vegan Films

We've told you what's wrong with eating animals and why veganism is so great. Here are some films that will show you more. You can find them, and others, on Youtube, Netflix, Amazon Video or their own websites.

Animal Rights: A Universal Declaration

Best Speech You Will Ever Hear by Gary Yourofsky

Called to Rescue

Carnage: Swallowing the Past

Cowspiracy: The Sustainability Secret

Deadly Dairy

Dominion

Earthlings

The End of Meat

The Game Changers

H.O.P.E. What You Eat Matters

Land of Hope and Glory

Meat The Truth

Okja

The Witness

You Will Never Look at Your Life in the Same Way Again by Ed Winters

For Animals *by Dean Bracher of Vegan Campaigns*

I spend a lot of time at animal sanctuaries; the places where different species are cared for and given the freedom to live, and in a world that recognises their value. These animals are not much different from you or I, well they are, but I've had many a game of football with Percy the pig and lost. Percy loves ball games. Before he came to the sanctuary, Percy had been raised like a dog and taken around on a lead. So when he arrived he would playfully nip at people's feet and legs and call out when left alone. You could see his previous life had given him certain personality traits that were unhelpful to him and those caring for him. But after time and attention, he showed his humour and that he wanted to be loved, like all of us, and to know that this world would not treat him badly, but would value his life and look after his needs.

Our individuality is important to us. We take for granted that we have choices and control over our lives. Being vegan for me means taking responsibility for your actions, knowing the consequences of them, and making choices that achieve positive results and save lives while at the same time enhancing your own life. It's about valuing equally the lives of other species and seeing their unique personalities. You can see that we all breathe and want freedom to make our own decisions. We want to take part in life and make sure that we care for those around us and leave the planet in a good state for future generations.

More and more people are seeing the reality of factory farms and the way animals are treated to produce all sorts of things that society deems necessary, but aren't. These bring the world no pleasure of any kind, only suffering; they just take and take and take until nothing is left. Our one planet, already fully populated with people and animals, doesn't need billions more using water, resources, and then having their lives ended so that more can be bred. There really seems no sense in this when we know that an individual animal is the same as us, has the same feelings and needs and wants what we want. These individuals would not choose to live in factory farms, or indeed in any farm. I went vegan to stop that and give the planet a rest and help the lives of all species.

If something is worth doing and we know it will make a difference, then why not? Visit an animal sanctuary and let a pig beat you at football, or a chicken perch on your shoulders, or stroke a sheep, and see them for who they really are and not what you've been told or taught.

I leave you with this: you have more power to change a bad situation than you realise, and when you make that decision, it will make this planet a better place.

> *"The animals of the world exist for their own reasons.*
> *They were not made for humans any more than black people*
> *were made for white, or women created for men."*
>
> Alice Walker

For the Environment *by Catherine Laurence BA, MSc*

Being vegan is not only kind and healthy but it's better for the environment too.

Of the total mass of mammals on Earth, food animals account for 60%, humans 36%, and wild animals just 4%. Over three-quarters of all agricultural land in the world is used for animal farming. For the United Kingdom that figure is 85%.

The world's one billion cows, and billions more sheep, pigs and chickens, outnumber humans by three to one. As well as grass, they eat 45% of the world's grain and up to 90% of the soya harvest. When converting grains and soya to protein and fat, most of the calories and protein are wasted.

Food animals drink more water than humans, and produce many times more waste, polluting rivers and underground water supplies. The intensive agriculture to grow their feed crops uses millions of litres of pesticides, not to mention fertilizer, which also run off into rivers.

As intensive agriculture and grazing reduce the amount of topsoil, land degrades and becomes less and less productive. More than 75% of Earth's land area is already degraded, and more than 90% could become degraded by 2050, with estimates anticipating up to one billion environmental refugees by 2050.

Food animals are the main sources of methane and nitrous oxide, the most powerful greenhouse gases, through their burps, farts and manure.

For decades humans have been cutting down forests worldwide, mainly for grazing and growing animal feed. Trees now cover just 9% of Northern Ireland, 10% of England, 15% of Wales and 19% of Scotland.

Plastic bags and food miles are topical environmental issues, but what we eat is more important than what it's packed in or where it comes from. In fact, while saying no to single-use bags and straws is an important step, the main source of ocean plastic pollution is discarded fishing gear from both 'wild-caught' and farmed fish – another reason among so many to say 'no' to sea food and 'yes' to sea life.

Our food choices are the most important aspect of our ecological footprint, a way that we interact with the environment every day. Eating vegan minimizes our impact. Plant-based diets require about one fifth as much land as omnivorous ones. This is good for the natural world and good for us. For example, it would allow enough reforestation to put the brakes on climate change, while restoring habitat to our threatened wildlife.

> *"I AM VEGAN. I don't eat animal products.*
> *I don't use any animal products because of ethical,*
> *environmental and climate reasons."*

> Greta Thunberg

The real population problem: livestock

Methane emissions per animal/human per year

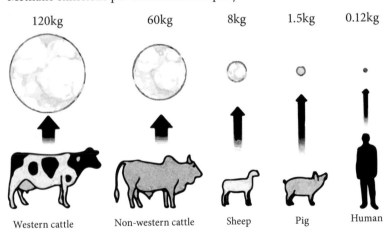

120kg	60kg	8kg	1.5kg	0.12kg
Western cattle	Non-western cattle	Sheep	Pig	Human

SOURCE: Nasa Goddard Institute for Space Studies

THE BIRTH OF MODERN VEGANISM

People have had a vegetarian, almost vegan, diet in some parts of the world for thousands of years. Around 500 B.C. the Greek mathematician and philosopher Pythagoras called on politicians to act justly in the highest degree by not hurting animals.

The social justice activist Jeremy Bentham compared human superiority over animals to racism as early as the 18th century. The Vegetarian Society was founded in Manchester in 1847. Throughout the 19th century, vegan pioneers in Britain and America, at that time known as strict or total vegetarians, discussed and debated the cruelty of the milk industry within the wider vegetarian movement.

The first vegan cookbook, *No Animal Food: Two Essays and 100 Recipes*, by Rupert Wheldon, was published in 1910.

In November 1944, the Vegan Society was created in the UK, with Donald Watson as its first secretary. Donald invented the word *vegan*, calling it "the beginning and end of veg-etari-an". Donald typed their newsletters, which started off with fewer than 30 subscribers.

In 1960 Jay and Freya Dinshah founded the American Vegan Society. Jay travelled widely to promote veganism and they organised annual conventions.

In 1965 the Plant Milk Society, later Plamil Foods, introduced soya milk to the UK. Led by Arthur Ling, who was also very active in the Vegan Society, and later by his son Adrian Ling, Plamil also pioneered vegan mayonnaise, an early attempt at cheese spread, and several kinds of chocolate.

Donald Watson with the first Vegan Society newsletter

Other groundbreaking and innovative vegan outreach organisations founded last century include Animal Aid (1977), People for the Ethical Treatment of Animals (PETA, 1980), Physicians Committee for Responsible Medicine (PCRM, 1985), and Vegetarians International Voice for Animals (Viva!, 1994).

In 1994 Louise Wallis, Chair of the Vegan Society, proposed World Vegan Day, celebrated on 1st November. This later became National Vegan Week, the week around 1st November including both weekends, and then World Vegan Month, the whole of November. It's a popular time to organise vegan outreach events and get coverage in newspapers and on local radio. This was taken to the next level by the Veganuary campaign, which every year supports hundreds of thousands of people to go vegan for January.

Thanks to the foundations laid in the 20th century by vegan campaigning and food pioneers, becoming vegan these days is easier than becoming vegetarian was 50 years ago. As more and more people go vegan or choose to eat more vegan food, vegan food is becoming available everywhere. With vegan food easily available, and A-list celebrities, politicians and business leaders jumping on the bandwagon, being vegan is becoming cool, fashionable and unstoppable.

CHAPTER 2
A Balanced Diet

by Scarlet Hughes, BSc (nutrition)

A vegan diet excludes all animal products, such as meat, dairy, eggs and honey.

The British Dietetic Association (BDA) is the UK's largest, and one of its most long-standing organisations that represents food and nutrition professionals, with over 9,000 members. The BDA has declared that a well-planned vegan diet can "support healthy living in people of all ages". It has renewed its Memorandum of Understanding with The Vegan Society to state that a balanced vegan diet can be enjoyed by children and adults, including during pregnancy and breastfeeding, if the nutritional intake is well planned.

Nowadays shop shelves are stocked with vegan sweets, pizzas, cakes, doughnuts, burgers, fish-style fillets and all sorts of ready meals. These are vegan from an ethical perspective, but are not necessarily the healthiest choice. Most are 'empty calories', meaning that besides energy, they provide little nutritional value. They can be highly processed, containing alarming amounts of refined sugar, sodium and saturated fat. Even high protein foods, such as soya or seitan based burgers, can be loaded with fat and salt. Cutting out animal products does not automatically lead to a balanced diet bursting with plant-based goodness. Does this mean that we should never consume manufactured foods?

A healthy and balanced diet is wholefood plant-based, avoiding processed foods (high in refined sugar, oil and salt, and low in fibre and micronutrients) and replacing them with food to be consumed as a whole. For example, whole apple rather than apple juice, roasted or steamed potato versus chips or a packet of crisps, wholemeal pasta rather than white pasta, home-made blended banana ice cream rather than ice cream with added refined sugar, and stir-fried vegetables with brown rice rather than shop-bought stir-fry with fried white rice.

There is evidence that eating this way has the power to help prevent heart disease, diabetes and various types of cancer (see chapter 7).

The word *vegan* on the product label or packaging can sometimes come with a hefty price tag, giving some people the impression that being vegan is expensive, whereas the healthier vegan foods are actually very cheap, such as beans, lentils, peas, wholegrain rice, and so on. For example, a homemade dal and rice dish will cost under £1 a portion to make, whereas you would typically spend over £5 if you bought this from a take-away or supermarket.

Although vegans consume a 100% plant-based diet, not all consume a wholefood plant-based diet. Our diet is more than just putting nutrients into our stomachs; food is a way in which we connect with people, culture and our past experiences. The plant-based alternatives mentioned above, such as burgers, allow people to easily adapt their current diet and facilitate the transition to a vegan diet. A great vegan diet is about getting the right balance, and we recommend that the processed products mentioned above should only be consumed in small or moderate amounts.

Changing to a vegan diet provides the opportunity to learn more about food. With adaptations to favourite recipes and seeking out new ones, you can gain a new appreciation and respect for what you eat.

A SAMPLE HEALTHY VEGAN DIET

We are all different and our nutritional requirements can vary and change depending on our age, gender and lifestyle. Public Health England's **Eatwell** guide is the general recommendation for the UK population. The version below, adapted by Plant-Based Health Professionals UK (PBHP, see chapter 7), is a great guide to confident transition to a balanced vegan diet and maintaining good health.

Note: the recommendations below are for the general population. If you suffer from any illness or health condition, please consult a health professional before transitioning to a vegan diet. There is a list on the PBHP website.

Starchy carbohydrates (potatoes, bread, rice, pasta etc)

This if your main source of energy. When you consume grains, choose whole grains when possible, as the process of refining grains removes

The Plant-Based Eatwell Guide

This is a plant-based adaptation of Public Health England's Eatwell guide (2016). It aims to help you transition to a healthy and sustainable diet. It shows food groups in the proportions that they should contribute to the overall diet.

6-8 a day

Water, plant-milks and drinks without sugar including tea and coffee all count

Limit fruit juice and/or smoothies to a total of 150ml a day

Choose wholegrain or higher fibre versions with less added fat, salt and sugar

Potatoes, bread, rice, pasta and other starchy carbohydrates

Rye Bread

Rice

Whole wheat pasta

Whole grain cereal

Potatoes

Quinoa & Buck-wheat

Porridge

Unhealthy products

Sauce

Crisps

Eat less often and only small amounts

Salt, sugar & fat

Flax seeds

Oil and fats

Choose unsaturated oils and use in small amounts

Plant-based dairy alternatives

Choose unsweetened calcium and vitamin D fortified versions

Plant based milk

Soya drink

Lentils

Beans reduced salt and sugar

Plant protein

Mixed seeds

Chick Peas

Tofu

Plain nuts

Peanut butter

Beans, pulses, peas, nuts, seeds and plant protein

Eat beans, peas and lentils, include one tbsp of ground flaxseed or chia seeds for essential omega-3 fats. Eat less subtitute meat

Raisins

Chopped tomatoes

Frozen peas

Eat at least 5 portions of a variety of fruit and vegetables every day

Check the label on packaged foods

Each serving (150g) contains

Energy 1046kJ 250kcal	Fat 3.0g	Saturates 1.3g	Sugars 34g	Salt 0.9g
	LOW	LOW	HIGH	MED
13%	4%	7%	38%	15%

of an adult's reference intake
Typical values (as sold) per 100g: 697kJ/ 167kcal

Choose foods lower in fat, salt and sugars

Vitamin B12

B12

National yeast flakes B12

Choose a reliable source of Vit. B12

Herbs, spices and fermented foods

Sauer-kraut

Vinegar

Add flavour and provide antioxidants and probiotics and are often anti-inflammatory

Per day 🌱 2000kcal 🌱 2500kcal = ALL FOOD + ALL DRINKS

certain nutrients such as dietary fibre, iron and some B vitamins. Options include brown rice, oats, whole wheat, whole grain pasta or bread, quinoa, buckwheat, amaranth and polenta.

Starchy vegetables such as sweet potatoes, pumpkin, cassava, yam, pumpkin and squashes are also a great source of carbohydrates.

Pulses, nuts, seeds and plant protein

There are plenty of plant sources of protein to be included in a vegan diet. Pulses, also known as legumes, include: beans, lentils, chickpeas and soya. These can be consumed cooked, or sprouted and made into paste, such as hummus. Nuts and seeds are also good sources of protein, as well as omega-3 (see later in this chapter).

Vegetables and fruits

A healthy diet should include plenty of fruit and vegetables. Aim for a minimum of five portions of fruit and vegetables each day. A portion is around 80g of fresh, canned or frozen vegetables. Opt for those without added sugar and salt.

The colour of each vegetable means they are rich in a different phytonutrient (explained below) and each has their own health benefits. All fruits and vegetables have their role to play. Green vegetables, for example, are a particularly good source of calcium, and cruciferous vegetables are particularly rich in sulphur-containing compounds called glucosinolates, which have been shown to be protective against certain types of cancer. Therefore, consume liberally and with as great a variety of colours as possible.

Examples of a rainbow of fruits and vegetables are:

Violet: blueberries, blackberries, red grapes, acai, fig, aubergine.

Green: pear, apple, avocado, kiwi fruit, cucumber, green beans, courgette, asparagus.
Green vegetables include spinach, cabbage, chard, pak choi, spring greens, kale, collards, broccoli, Romanesco, cauliflower, Brussels sprouts, lettuce, rocket.

Yellow: banana, pineapple, mango, durian, pear, yellow pepper, corn.

Orange: orange, clementine, satsuma, apricot, persimmon (kaki), papaya, pepper, grapefruit, carrot, sweet potato, squash, pumpkin.

Red: watermelon, strawberries, raspberries, pomegranate, cherries, tomato, beetroot, radish, red pepper, chilli.

Plant-based dairy alternatives

Fortified soya and other plant milks and yogurt are a good source of calcium and vitamin D in a vegan diet. Give preference to the ones with no added sugars, due to their effect on insulin levels (see Carbohydrates below).

Oils and fats

Consume olive, coconut and other oils sparingly as these are processed and have lower nutritional value than whole olives or coconuts. If you use oil for cooking, then the most accessible one is rapeseed (canola) oil rather than sunflower oil, as the former is a good source of omega-3 (see omega-3 section below). Rapeseed oil is usually labelled vegetable oil in supermarkets and has a picture of yellow rapeseed flowers on the label. Two tablespoons provides your daily requirement of omega-3 essential fatty acids. Hempseed oil is also a good choice.

Wholefood sources of healthy fats are avocado, olives, nuts and seeds. A good sized portion is 2 tablespoons of seeds such as pumpkin, flaxseed (linseed), sesame or chia, or 30-60g of nuts, including almonds, walnuts, cashews, and Brazil. This amount can also be consumed as spreads and dressings by using tahini (sesame spread) or nut butters.

Herbs and spices

There's no minimum requirement for these but just small amounts are a great way to add flavour and give health benefits as they are rich in phytochemicals with antioxidant and anti-inflammatory properties. For example, turmeric contains curcumin, a highly anti-inflammmatory compound.

Fermented foods

No minimum required but fermented food such as kimchi, sauerkraut, vegan yogurt and tempeh (a meat replacer made from fermented soya beans) are rich in probiotic bacteria that contribute to a healthy gut microbiome. The health benefits include an improved immune system, digestion, and discovered most recently, mental health.

Supplements

Vitamin B12 is essential and cannot be found in plant foods; therefore fortified foods and supplements are highly recommended. (see B12 section below)

Here are some wholefood menu ideas:

Breakfasts

Muesli: home-made blend, or bought from a wholefood shop. Many branded ones are high in sugar, and some even contain milk powder.
Porridge or overnight oats: with toppings such as dried and fresh fruits, seeds, nuts, etc.
Wholegrain toast with scrambled tofu
Oatcakes: with nut butter, banana, vegan cheese, olive spread etc.
Smoothies: A few ideas are green smoothies (made with spinach/kale, banana, pear, soya yogurt and protein powder), berry smoothies (made with berries, banana, apple).
Smoothie bowls: A thicker smoothie made with frozen banana. You can add toppings such as jumbo oats, nut butter, fresh and dried fruits, etc.
Fruit with plant-based yogurt
Breakfast bars: if you're on the move, made with seeds, nuts, oats, or coconut.

Midday and evening meals

Pasta with tomato sauce: This can be creative, with lots of vegetables such as onions, broccoli, mushrooms, olives, peppers, chili, and courgette. You can also add a protein source such as lentils or soya chunks.
Lasagne: using the same tomato sauce with vegetables, lentils and white sauce. For a béchamel white sauce recipe see chapter 3.
Vegetable curry: can be made with vegetables of your choice and a protein source such as chickpeas or frozen peas.
Mexican bean burrito: with plant-based yogurt or vegan cheese.
Falafel: with hummus, pita, and cucumber & tomato salad.
Wraps: filled with hummus, avocado, green leafy vegetables, beans and butternut squash.
Sandwiches: Try mashed avocado, tomato, lettuce, and chilli flakes; hummus, cucumber and marinated tofu; or mashed chickpeas with shredded cabbage, mustard and dill. If you have less time, then vegan ham or cream cheese from a supermarket can be useful.
Oatcakes: with any of the above.
Soups: are a brilliant way to get loads of nutrients in a filling, low-fat way. Try making a big batch of miso, vegetable, lentil or tomato and freeze in individual portions. Tinned soups can be very high in salt and also contain bulking ingredients, such as modified

starch, that serve no purpose other than to increase the profit margin for the manufacturer. Home-made soups are simple, satisfying, cheap and usually more nutritious.

Sushi rolls: can be made with a variety of vegetables, such as avocado, carrot, cucumber, pickled ginger and red peppers.

Tofu or cashew nut and veg stir-fry: with brown rice.

Lentil dal: with brown rice.

Rice and beans: with plantain.

Salad bowls: can have a type of green leaf as a base (watercress, lettuce, rocket), one type of grain (such as buckwheat, quinoa, millet), one protein source (beans, chickpeas, sprouted lentils) and three vegetables (sweet potato, tomato, asparagus, grated carrots, etc.) and a seed or nut dressing (tahini or peanut butter with lemon juice, seasoned with herbs).

Vegan pizza: with a homemade wholemeal base, and drizzled with olive oil.

Desserts

Vegan ice cream: made with frozen banana, blended strawberries or cacao or with a little cinnamon.

Vegan yogurt: with fruits, nuts, seeds or nut butter.

Pineapple sorbet: just mash pineapple and freeze it.

Dark chocolate

Banana bread

Peanut butter cookies

Snacks

Small handful of nuts or seeds.

Fresh fruits.

Frozen berries.

A glass of almond milk.

Oatcake or rice cakes: with one or a combination of the following toppings: avocado, banana, nut butter, vegan cheese, hummus.

Vegetable sticks with dips: such as hummus.

Snack bars: made with seeds, nuts, oats and coconut. You can make them yourself.

Drink plenty of *water* according to the weather and your level of physical activity. It's not a cliché, water is necessary for our body to function.

Additional tips

Season: foods with herbs (oregano, basil, parsley, rosemary, etc) and spices (cinnamon, turmeric, ginger, nutmeg). Spices and herbs are highly nutritious and a great way to change the taste of dishes. A little goes a long way.

Other ways to add flavours to dishes are by using yeast extract (such as Marmite or Vegemite), yeast flakes, lemon, ground or flaked dried seaweed, or a spoonful of tahini or peanut butter.

Dressings: for salads can be made whole food using tahini, nut butters, soya sauce, avocado, lemon, herbs and spices.

Herbal teas: can replace caffeine and sugary drinks. Some have health benefits , for example rooibos is rich in antioxidants and the menthol in peppermint is a muscle relaxant, while passion flower can help to reduce anxiety and improve sleep.

Limit salt: and use seasoning instead. If you must add salt, use iodised salt, to prevent iodine deficiency, or add a splash of tamari soya sauce or some miso to give a salty taste.

Consume as much variety: as possible and rotate the green leafy vegetables, seeds, nuts, legumes, and so on. Each plant has a unique combination of nutrients and phytonutrients.

Avoid food waste: We discard a lot of edible food, such as broccoli stalks and cauliflower leaves. UK households annually throw away 4.5 million tonnes of food. 70% of such wasted nutritious food we could have consumed in soups or added to any vegetable dish.

If avoiding oil: you can sauté in small amounts of water. Another option is to use tahini (or nut butter) diluted with lemon juice (to make it acidic) and water for basting when roasting, or for salad dressing.

Bulk/Batch Cooking

Make large pots or batches of soups, lasagne, pulses, grains, and vegetables, and freeze them in small containers. When you are ready to eat them, just warm up in the oven or microwave. This can be time saving, money saving and also more likely to be healthier for you than shop-bought ready meals or takeaways.

WHAT TO EAT: WHICH FOODS CONTAIN WHICH NUTRIENTS

Below are tables showing the nutrients everyone needs in their diet and their best plant sources.

Macronutrients

Macronutrients are nutrients which we need in large amounts, made up from the bulk of the food we eat.

MACRONUTRIENT	GOOD SOURCES	ROLE
PROTEIN	Pulses, grains (inc. quinoa, oats, spelt), soya products, seitan, nuts and seeds	Building blocks of cells and tissues, needed for growth and repair. Can also be used as a source of energy.
CARBOHYDRATES	Whole grains (inc. oats, brown rice, pasta, rye), wholemeal bread, starchy vegetables, fruits (especially banana, plantain, mango)	Main source of energy
FATS	Avocado, coconut, seeds (esp. flaxseeds, chia, hemp), olives, nuts, spreads such as tahini, nut butters	Help absorb and carry various vitamins and energy to cells. Essential fatty acids are needed for our skin and brain. Can be used as a source of energy.

We will look at the macronutrients in more detail further down.

Micronutrients

Micronutrients are nutrients which we need in small amounts.

VITAMIN	GOOD SOURCES	ROLE
VITAMIN A (BETA-CAROTENE)	Carrot, sweet potato, leafy green vegetables, butternut squash, apricots, tomatoes.	Helps the immune system (body's natural defence against illness and infection) work properly. Vision and keeping skin and lining of some parts of the body, such as nose, healthy
B VITAMINS B1 THIAMIN B2 RIBOFLAVIN B3 NIACIN B5 PANTOTHENIC ACID B6 PYRIDOXINE B9 FOLIC ACID	Yeast extract, whole grains, wholemeal bread, banana, berries, pumpkin seeds, nuts (Especially Brazil nuts, hazelnuts and almonds), broccoli and lentils	Release and use of energy from foods, nervous system, and healthy red blood cells
VITAMIN B12	Fortified non-dairy milks***, supplements, fortified yeast extract	Healthy red blood cells and nervous system. Assists the use of energy and folate (naturally occurring form of folic acid).
VITAMIN C	Peppers, citrus fruits*, leafy green vegetables**, strawberries, tomatoes, broccoli	Protects cells, maintain healthy skin, bones, blood vessels, helps with wound healing. Assists with absorption of iron.
VITAMIN D	Sunlight, fortified breakfast cereals, fortified non-dairy milks***, and mushrooms if grown under UV light	Helps calcium absorption for healthy bones and teeth. Supports immune system.
VITAMIN E	Avocado, seeds, tomatoes, nuts (especially almonds)	Strengthens the immune system and helps maintain healthy skin and eyes
VITAMIN K	Leafy green vegetables**, broccoli, Brussels sprouts, asparagus, peas	Needed for blood clotting, helping wounds to heal.

* Citrus fruits: orange, grapefruit, lime and lemon
**Leafy green vegetables: kale, spinach, spring (collard) greens, Swiss chard, watercress, rocket, lettuce
*** Fortified non-dairy milks: soya, almond, hazelnut, coconut, oat, etc.

MINERALS	GOOD SOURCES	ROLE
IRON	Dark leafy greens, beans, lentils, peas, prunes and juice, bran flakes, soya products, seeds (esp. pumpkin), fortified products, turmeric, dried apricots, broccoli	Needed for growth and development. Used to make haemoglobin, a protein in blood cells that carries oxygen around the body
MAGNESIUM	Dark leafy greens, black beans, peas, nuts (specially almonds), whole grains, dried fruits, dark chocolate	Metabolism, muscle and nerve functions. Helps turn food into energy and function of parathyroid glands (which produce hormones for bone health)
CALCIUM	Leafy green vegetables (except oxalate rich such as spinach), fortified products, okra, almonds, sesame seeds, beans, lentils and chickpeas	Builds bones and teeth. Regulating muscle contraction (inc. heart beat) and ensures normal blood clotting process. (See below for more on calcium)
IODINE	Dried seaweed, iodized salt and Vecon vegetable stock	Makes thyroid hormones which help keep cells and metabolic rate (speed at which chemical reactions take place in the body) healthy
ZINC	Beans, lentils, soya products, seeds (esp. pumpkin), nuts, oats, whole grains, green leafy vegetables	Helps with wound healing and carbohydrate, fat and protein metabolism. Essential in making new cells and enzymes (proteins that act as biological catalysts to accelerate chemical reactions, such as breaking down food)
MANGANESE	Hazelnuts, brown rice, pecans, chickpeas, oats, avocado, banana,	Helps make and activate some of the enzymes in the body.
SELENIUM	Brazil nuts, sunflower seeds, whole grains	Helps prevent damage to cells and tissues. Essential to the immune system and in reproduction

POTASSIUM	Leafy green vegetables, bananas, beans, nuts, Brussels sprouts, aubergine, melon, ginger root	Helps control the balance of fluid in the body, and also helps our muscles (including heart) work properly
OTHERS (COPPER, MOLYBDENUM, PHOSPHORUS, CHROMIUM)	Cereal grains, nuts, potatoes carrots,	These help with functioning of our body. Only needed in very small amounts and widely available in a healthy plant-based diet.

A well varied, wholefood plant-based diet will supply all the above nutrients. There are special concerns about the nutrients discussed in the next part of this chapter.

VEGAN NUTRITION IN DETAIL

Here comes the science. If you find science a bit overwhelming, then you could skip ahead to the next chapter and get started right away on shopping and making some delicious vegan food. You can refer to this chapter when relatives or friends start asking you: "Where do you get your protein or calcium or iron from?"

A balanced diet should meet the individual body's minimum requirements of nutrients to perform all biological processes, without oversupplying calories. Different people have different requirements, depending on age, gender, level of activity, pregnancy and breast feeding.

Types of macronutrients

Carbohydrate

Carbohydrates, as found in rice or pasta, are a group of chemical structures called saccharides that include starch, sugars and cellulose (fibre). When digested, they are broken down into the simple sugar glucose to be used by our cells as their main source of energy. Glucose combines with oxygen from breathing to create water and carbon dioxide, at the same time releasing energy for movement and heat.

Carbohydrates are stored in our cells as the large molecule glycogen a multi-branched polysaccharide of glucose, to be converted to glucose and used for energy when required.

The British Dietetic Association, the professional association for UK dietitians, recommends that 26 - 45% of our energy consumption should come from carbohydrates; although it really depends on the level of activity and each person's energy use.

When we consume high sugar foods, the glucose level in our blood increases rapidly, so we say that these foods have a high glycemic index. To balance this effect, our body produces and releases insulin from the pancreas. Insulin works like a key to unlock cells, so allowing glucose in the blood to enter them and be stored there until it is needed, thus reducing the level of glucose in the blood.

Diabetes Type 2 occurs when our cells are resistant to the insulin produced and therefore our body cannot effectively regulate its blood glucose level. Foods that are low in fibre and high in carbohydrate, such as table sugar and white bread, have a high glycemic index and rapidly raise and spike blood glucose levels, while other foods that are high in fibre such as fruits and whole grains have a lower glycemic index and as such blood glucose does not spike as high. Therefore, it is best to consume foods high in fibre.

Fibre is a type of carbohydrate, and there are two types: insoluble fibre, found in beans, green leafy vegetables and peas; and soluble fibre, found in fruits, vegetables, oats, rye, root vegetables. Fibre rich foods are generally less calorie dense, more bulky and help you to feel fuller for longer.

Fibre slows down and reduces the absorption of energy in the food we consume, thus not increasing our glucose and insulin level.

Fibre is also essential to keep our gut microbes healthy. It assists the digestive system by bulking up and softening stools, thus reducing the chance of constipation and increasing the diversity of our gut microbiota. A diet low in fibre and high in fat, i.e. ketogenic, leads to constipation and low numbers of gut microbiota. There is a lot of interesting research into gut microbiota and we are still learning more about its role in relation to metabolism and weight management.

The recommended daily amount for fibre is 30g and a whole food plant-based diet will easily provide that. Fibre should be consumed in its naturally occurring state, found in fruits, including apples, pears, mangos, and in pulses, including beans, lentils, chickpeas, and not as processed bran added to things like refined breakfast cereals.

Protein

Proteins are the building blocks for our cells and tissues and are made up of a combination of 21 amino acids. Our body is not capable of producing eight or nine (depending on the person): histidine, isoleucine, leucine, lysine, methionine, phenylalanine, threonine, tryptophan, valine. Three others are also required by infants and growing children: arginine, cysteine, tyrosine. These are called **essential amino acids** and we must acquire them through diet. Plant foods contain all the essential amino acids we need; therefore, it is highly unlikely a plant-based diet will be deficient in protein.

All amino acids are available in plants, but in different ratios. As a general rule, grains are high in methionine and low in lysine, while pulses are high in lysine. Therefore, it is necessary to eat both sources of protein to obtain a 'complete' range of protein, though not necessarily at the same meal, as our body contains an amino acid 'pool'. Some of the world's classic dishes reflect this, such as rice with beans.

The daily requirement is about 10% of calories from protein, or approximately 0.8 g of protein per kg of bodyweight. 1g protein contains 4 kcalories of energy. (1 cookbook Calorie = 1kcal). Therefore, a 70kg person should aim for a daily average 56g of protein. Protein requirement varies in people. Those recovering from illness or surgery or who regularly lift weights may have a higher requirement as it is needed to build and repair cells, especially muscles.

Protein is found in large quantities in beans, soya, lentils, peas, quinoa, nuts and dark leafy green vegetables. Best sources are from soya beans (edamame), which contain 18g per 100g cooked which is 21g per 200 calories, and pulses where 100g of cooked lentils and beans contain between 8 and 9g, which is 15g per 200 calories.

Although animal protein contains all the essential amino acids, it is not the best source due to adverse health risks. By eating a variety of vegan protein sources, you will get all the amino acids necessary to build protein for muscle and cells. Plant-based sources of protein have benefits compared to animal protein as they are low in fat and high in fibre and in addition contain (cancer-busting) phytochemicals, which all benefit health and disease prevention.

Fats

There are four types of fats: saturated, trans unsaturated, monounsaturated and polyunsaturated.

Saturated fat is usually solid at room temperature and can be found in some plant foods such as coconut oil and palm oil, but is more widely present in animal foods, such as meat, eggs and dairy. High consumption of saturated fat is harmful to us and its consumption has been linked to a number of diseases (See chapter 7).

Trans unsaturated fats, or trans fats, are also solid at room temperature. They are found naturally in small amounts in animal products, such as butter. Artificial trans fats, also known as partially hydrogenated fats, are vegetable oils that have been industrially processed to make them solid and give them a longer shelf life. These have been linked to an increased risk of heart disease. Trans fats used to be found in processed foods such as frozen pizza, vegetable shortening and margarine, pastries, doughnuts, cakes and biscuits, including vegan ones. The UK food industry agreed to phase them out in 2008, and since 2012 they make up less than 1% of fat in processed foods in the UK.

Monounsaturated fats are liquid at room temperature and are found in plant foods, such as avocado, nuts, seeds, and vegetable oils, in particular olive oil. They have been shown to lower low-density lipoprotein (LDL), the bad cholesterol in our body.

Polyunsaturated fats, found in the same plant foods as monounsaturated fats, are also liquid at room temperature. They include the essential fatty acids omega-3 and omega-6, both of which our body cannot make and therefore must obtain from food.

Essential fatty acids

There are two essential fats we need and they both come from plants. Omega-6 is easily obtained in a vegan diet from foods such as nuts, seeds, oils and foods made with them.

However, omega-3 is something we all need to pay attention to so that we ensure there is enough in our diet. In terms of practical advice it is recommended to minimise omega-6 rich foods such as corn, soya and sunflower oil (which tend to be abundant in the diet and can compete with omega-3 for enzymes in the body), and regularly consume healthy omega-3 rich foods. These include walnuts (7 a day), or at least 1 tablespoon of flaxseed, hemp or chia seeds a day, or 2tbs of rapeseed (canola) oil or soyabean oil.

If you regularly cook with sunflower oil, simply switching to rapeseed oil is a good idea.

Flaxseeds should be ground in a coffee grinder or high speed food processor for proper absorption; otherwise, they can pass straight through you. They can, for example, be mixed in with hot or cold breakfast cereals or muesli or smoothies, or added into recipes when baking.

Omega-3

There are three types of omega-3 fatty acids: alpha-linolenic acid (ALA), eicosapentaenoic acid (EPA) and docosahexaenoic acid (DHA). We only need ALA as our body converts ALA into EPA and DHA, though only in small amounts, and the amounts converted can vary considerably between people. There is plenty of ALA in the plant foods mentioned above. A small number of vegans might benefit from taking a vegan EPA and DHA supplement made from algae.

EPA and DHA are used in every system in the body including cell membranes, the brain and nervous system. There is some evidence that EPA may help with depression. Omega 3 has the ability to lower inflammation, protects against heart disease (Yokoyama M, et. al., 2007) and potentially prostate cancer (Leitzmann MF, et. al., 2004).

Non-vegans get EPA and DHA from eating oily fish or a fish oil supplement, or from "omega-3 eggs" produced by chickens that are fed flaxseed and sometimes fish oil. Fish do not make omega-3 but get it by eating algae, or by eating smaller fish that eat algae. Oily fish contain harmful chemicals including mercury, dioxins and PCBs (polychlorinated biphenyls) and there are not enough fish left in the sea for everyone in the world to eat them regularly. There are no such safety or sustainability issues with directly consuming plant sources of omega-3. And no animal suffering.

Vitamins and Minerals

Vitamins are compounds, and **minerals** are elements, which assist our cells to do what they are supposed to do. A balanced diet provides plenty of nutrients, but there a few which we should be vigilant to ensure we get enough of:

Iodine

Iodine is an essential nutrient for a healthy thyroid. Hyperthyroidism (overactive thyroid gland) symptoms include weight loss, enlarged thyroid gland (goitre), increased heart rate, anxiety, difficulty sleeping. Hypothyroidism (underactive thyroid gland) symptoms include weight gain, depression, tiredness, sensitivity to cold.

Iodine is typically undesirably low in UK vegan diets as UK soil is low in iodine, and the biggest source is dairy products, since cows are given iodine. The best plant sources are seaweeds, such as kelp, and iodised salt. These can be consumed as vegan sushi or crumbled and added as topping for salads or other dishes such as tofu and green vegetable soups.

Intakes in the range 100-300 micrograms per day are desirable, though intakes up to 500 micrograms per day are probably not harmful. If taking supplements, go for about 100-150 micrograms per day, to give a total intake of 150-200 micrograms per day. The VEG1 supplement from The Vegan Society contains an average of 150 micrograms, so one tablet a day provides about the right amount.

Vitamin B12

Vitamin B12 is important for nerve and blood cells, producing DNA, recycling the waste amino acid homocysteine, and burning fats, proteins and carbohydrates for energy, thus preventing fatigue. Major B12 deficiency can lead to irreversible neurological damage. Lesser deficiency causes high homocysteine levels in the blood which can contribute to heart disease.

No plant or animal (including humans) can make vitamin B12. It is made only by certain bacteria and archaea (similar to bacteria). Animal products tend to be the biggest source of B12 in a non-vegan diet as animals are usually supplemented with B12 in their diet or consume bacteria if they are grass fed. Deficiency is more common in vegans and people older than 50 years, but many non-vegans have a deficiency, due to low absorption of this vitamin.

The UK's Department of Health recommended dietary allowance is 2.4 mcg daily. Our vegan diet must contain a regular source of B12 in the form of fortified foods or a supplement.

If getting B12 from fortified foods, you should aim to consume three servings of B12 fortified products such as non-dairy milk, breakfast cereals, margarine, yogurt, yeast flakes, or yeast extract, to get a minimum of 3mcg a day.

If the B12 source is from supplements, to ensure adequate absorption, healthy individuals without deficiency should take a supplement with at least 10mcg daily, but preferably 50mcg daily, due to high level of deficiency in the population. This is in line with top vegan research expert Dr Michael Greger's latest recommendation towards the end of 2020 at nutritionfacts.org. Furthermore, Dr Greger recommends 1,000mcg per day for seniors and those suffering from a deficiency. If taking a supplement daily is not suitable for your lifestyle, a supplement with at least 2,000mcg can be taken weekly. For severe deficiency, as a last resort a doctor may also prescribe B12 injections.

Cyanocobalamin is the most stable form of B12 and should be taken as a chewable or liquid supplement for best absorption. Daily tiny doses have the same effect as one huge weekly dose. Frequent tiny doses are fairly well absorbed. As the dose increases, the proportion absorbed declines. Our body excretes any excess.

B12 tablets should be chewed, not swallowed whole, as saliva contains a B12 binding protein that helps transport B12 safely through the digestive tract, massively increasing the amount absorbed.

For convenience, many vegans take the Vegan Society's VEG1 supplement daily. As well as 25mcg of B12, this also includes vitamin D, iodine and selenium. Or take another vegan B12 or B-complex or multivitamin supplement, of which there are many.

For more detailed reference information about vitamin B12, read the Vegan Society website page *What Every Vegan Should Know About Vitamin B12*, or watch the B12 videos at nutritionfacts.org.

Calcium

The UK recommended daily calcium intake for adults is 700mg.

Calcium is required for good bone health. However, weight bearing exercise, just like for muscles, is the biggest contributor to bone health. Vitamins D and K, plus magnesium and phosphorous, are also necessary for healthy bones.

Excellent plant sources of calcium are almonds, broccoli, most greens, fresh and dried fruit, tahini, tofu and fortified products such as bread, soya milk or yogurt. These foods not only contain calcium, but also vitamin K, magnesium and phosphorous. And unlike milk they do not contain saturated fat and cholesterol, antibiotics, pesticides, blood or pus.

The green vegetables spinach and chard are high in oxalate, an anti-nutrient that binds to calcium and prevents its absorption. These are still healthy, good foods but just not excellent sources of calcium, so alternate them with other greens such as kale, watercress, broccoli, pak choi and green beans to ensure good calcium absorption.

Vitamin D

Vitamin D deficiency causes osteoporosis (brittle bones) and osteopenia (bone loss before osteoporosis) and it's no more common in vegans than meat eaters. It has also been linked with rheumatoid arthritis and infectious diseases.

Vitamin D is manufactured in the body by exposing at least the head and hands to small, regular amounts of strong sunlight. Sunblock cream stops natural vitamin D production. There is no official minimum requirement, but 15 minutes sun a day on the face and hands should do it.

During the winter months, where we get less sunlight, consume fortified foods, such as breakfast cereals and bread, and it may be prudent to take a supplement. If supplementing, aim for a daily intake of at least 25mcg or 1,000 IU (international units).

Iron

Iron is used to produce the substance haemoglobin that red blood cells use to carry oxygen from our lungs to the body's tissues. There is normally plenty of iron in a vegan diet.

Iron-deficiency anaemia symptoms include tiredness and lack of energy, shortness of breath, heart palpitations and pale skin. Iron deficiency is a concern for women in general and deficiency is common in both vegans and non-vegans due to blood loss.

The recommended daily amount (RDA) of iron is 8.7mg for adult men and for women over 50, and 14.8mg for pre-menopausal women.

The best sources of iron are pulses, nuts, seeds, and greens, especially leafy green vegetables. Dried fruit, whole grains and berries are also good sources. Consuming those foods with a food rich in vitamin C at the same meal (such as lemon or orange juice, tomatoes and green leafy vegetables) will improve absorption of iron.

Phytonutrients, beyond vitamins

Plant foods contain phytochemicals such as carotenoids, polyphenols and flavonoids. These have been shown to possess health-promoting properties, such as acting as anti-inflammatories and antioxidants.

Isolated nutrients in pills can only cure or prevent a specific deficiency. Plant foods contain many more than just the nutrients mentioned above. For example, the substance that gives the red foods their colour (such as tomatoes, peppers, apples and strawberries) is called lycopene, an antioxidant that helps reduce the risk of certain cancers including prostate cancer. The dark colours of grapes, blueberries, and beetroot are caused by anthocyanin, which improves blood circulation, and has anti-inflammatory and anti-tumour properties. Green vegetables contain chlorophyll, which acts as a detoxifier in cells and protects them and DNA from free radicals. It also protects the heart, and has an anticancer effect.

Nutrients and phytochemicals interact and work together, meaning that each food is a non-random complex, working synergistically for the benefit of both the plant and the eater. Whole plant foods contain hundreds, perhaps thousands, of phytonutrients, some identified, many not, which work together to promote health, especially prevention of cancer and heart disease. These nutrients are not found in animal products.

ANIMAL PRODUCTS, HEALTH AND FAKE SCIENCE

Meat and processed meats increase the risk of colorectal cancer (WCRF Report). In addition, they are high in saturated fat, which is a risk factor for heart disease.

Dairy products are also high in saturated fat. Although the fat can be removed to create low-fat dairy products, the removed dairy fat is inevitably still consumed by someone somewhere else in products such as ice cream, butter and baked goods. Dairy also poses an increased risk of ovarian and prostate cancer.

Eliminating dairy products does not increase the risk of osteoporosis, since calcium is well supplied by plant foods. Indeed, populations with the highest consumption of dairy products have the highest rates of osteoporosis.

Eggs are high in cholesterol and associated with increased risk of heart disease, stroke, breast cancer and prostate cancer.

In December 2019 vegan doctors at the Physicians Committee for Responsible Medicine exposed how the egg industry has been attempting to distort the science and mislead the public, press and policy makers about the clear relationship between eggs and heart disease. They have been funding faulty studies that skew the interpretation of the results, for example, concluding that "eggs have no effect on cholesterol" even though this contradicts their actual data. In reality: "According to a 2019 meta-analysis, eating an egg each day raises LDL (bad) cholesterol by about nine points." Also: "Of 153 studies analysed in the *American Journal of Lifestyle Medicine* report, 139 showed that eggs raise blood cholesterol. No studies reported significant net decreases in cholesterol concentrations."

This is just one example of how animal agriculture funds bad science to attempt to confuse us about the reality, which is the catastrophic damage to our health that their products cause.

Animal products, in particular **fish**, contain dioxins, polychlorinated biphenyls (PCBs, highly toxic industrial compounds), mercury and other pollutants which are harmful to our health.

Not to mention, non-organic animal products contain hormones and antibiotics.

Carbohydrates are unfairly criticised by a few people who follow a low-carb, high-fat **'ketogenic'** diet such as Atkins or Paleo. Such diets put the body in a state of ketosis, where there is no glucose available and therefore it burns fat for energy. Ketosis starts a few days after you stop consuming carbohydrate rich foods, and has side-effects such as headache, tiredness and constipation. Keto tends to be used by people who want to lose weight fast, but is low in nutrients, and deficiency of selenium and vitamin C has been seen in its followers. (Carlton J B., 2010). In contrast, a plant-based diet is full of nutrient dense, low calorie foods such as beans, fruits and vegetables. Admittedly, a ketogenic diet has shown benefits for some people suffering from epilepsy, but it needs to be carefully supervised to prevent side-effects, such as nutritional deficiencies, and has to maintain a good gut microbiome. This diet is also not easy to maintain (Ye F, et al. 2015) and is no more effective at achieving weight loss than any other type of dietary restriction. Quite apart from the long-term health issues, getting almost all calories from animal products is cruel, and completely unsustainable. If everyone in the world ate that way, we would need three planets just to grow all the animal feed.

VEGAN HEALTH WEBSITES, FILMS AND BOOKS

The science of vegan diets is constantly being updated as new research is published. Detailed information can be found on the following websites:

NutritionFacts.org (vegan doctors and scientists)

PlantBasedHealthProfessionals.com
(UK doctors, dietitians and nutritionists)

PCRM.org (vegan doctors in USA)

VeganHealth.org (dietitians)

VeganSociety.com

Vrg.org/nutrition

Viva-avida.com by Scarlet Hughes. Instagram: @scarlet_vegan_

Vegan health documentary films

A Delicate Balance: The Truth
Eating You Alive
Food Choices
Forks Over Knives
The Game Changers
Got The Facts On Milk? (Also known as *The Milk Documentary*)
The Invisible Vegan
Uprooting the Leading Causes of Death, Michael Greger MD
Vegucated
What the Health

Vegan health books

For more about these authors, see chapter 7.

How Not To Die: Discover the Foods Scientifically Proven to Prevent and Reverse Disease, Michael Greger MD, 2015.

Plant Based Nutrition and Health, Stephen Walsh PhD, The Vegan Society, 2003.

Prevent and Reverse Heart Disease, Caldwell Esselstyn M.D., 2007.

Vegan for Life, Jack Norris RD and Virginia Messina RD, 2nd edition 2020

Becoming Vegan, Brenda Davis and Vesanto Melina, 2014.

Vegan Savvy: The Expert's Guide to Nutrition on a Plant-based Diet, Azmina Govindji R.D., December 2020.

The Plant Power Doctor: A simple prescription for a healthier you, Gemma Newman M.D. (British vegan GP), January 2021

The Plant-Based Diet Revolution: 28 days to a happier gut and a healthier you, Alan Desmond M.D. (British vegan consultant gastroenterologist) and Bob Andrew, January 2021.

Books for vegan parents

Feeding Your Vegan Child – a practical guide to plant-based nutrition, Sandra Hood R.D., publication spring 2021.

Your Complete Vegan Pregnancy, Reed Mangels R.D., 2019.

Nourish: The Definitive Plant-Based Nutrition Guide for Familes, Brenda Davis R.D., December 2020.

CHAPTER 3
How to Eat Vegan

There are two approaches to this.

1. Kitchen techniques: Learn to cook a range of staple vegan dishes, then improvise and experiment as you get more confident, or

2. Convenience foods for busy people: Get your food intake as quickly and conveniently as possible, with minimal cooking.

This chapter deals with both approaches.

KITCHEN TECHNIQUES

Basic Equipment

Whether you're a student with just a couple of gas or electric rings, a microwave and a supermarket down the road, or a lawyer with a huge farmhouse kitchen and your own organic vegetable garden, you'll find it pretty easy to create tasty vegan meals. All you need is:

- Vegetable knife – a chopping knife with an 8, 9 or 10 inch (20, 22 or 25cm) blade
- Paring knife – a 3" to 4" or 8cm-10cm blade, for those fiddly jobs
- Serrated knife – ideal for tomatoes and bread
- Chopping board – wood, bamboo or plastic are much better than glass or pyrex. Wood tends to be self-sterilising, whereas plastic can be put in a dishwasher. Glass or pyrex ones will blunt your knives quickly.
- Peeler
- Grater
- Set of saucepans
- Frying pan – we recommend a cast iron one, for good heat distribution, although some people much prefer cheaper, non-stick ones
- Wooden spoon for stirring
- Colander for draining pasta and salad leaves

It's a great idea to get a hand blender and a food processor, as these will enable you to make soup, hummus and other dips. Many people have high-powered "bullet"-style blenders these days for smoothies, soups and sauces. They take up very little worktop space compared to traditional blenders. A wok will enable you to create stir-fries easily, and a spatula will make pancakes and fried breakfasts easier. With a microwave oven you can freeze, defrost and reheat portions of food very quickly and conveniently.

Ingredients

Vegan cuisine is based on a wide range of foods from around the world. The general principle is carbohydrates, such as rice, couscous, pasta (including gluten-free non-wheat pastas such as corn, flax, spelt), quinoa or noodles, served with some kind of vegetable and pulse-based stew such as curry, ratatouille, or satay which is an Indonesian sauce that typically contains peanuts. This way of cooking can take a bit of getting used to if you grew up thinking that a meal should centre on meat with vegetables on the side.

Here are some suggestions for a set of staple vegan dishes that you can adapt according to your personal tastes and what you have in the cupboard.

Ronny's Recipes and Kitchen Techniques

Spicy Tomato Sauce

Chop and gently fry half an onion per person, in olive oil or vegetable oil, until the onions go soft and start to stick together. Part way through, add a clove of garlic per person, a pinch of salt and a little black pepper. Add your choice of spices, such as cumin (for an earthy flavour,) mustard seeds (for depth and a little sharpness), paprika (for a smoky, earthy flavour and intense colour), turmeric (a superfood with an earthy, slightly bitter flavour), cinnamon (gives a hot, sweet, aromatic flavour), and chilli or cayenne pepper for a spicy heat.

Add half a tin of chopped tomatoes per person. Stir well, bring to the boil, and then simmer for at least ten minutes. Add a little soya sauce, yeast extract or vegetable stock for depth of flavour. The longer the sauce is simmered, the sweeter and richer it gets, as the starch in the tomatoes is turned into sugar.

If using this as the base for a chilli, add a little cacao powder or melted dark chocolate. If using for a curry, make it quite oily.

Add whatever vegetables and pulses you like. The pulses must be cooked separately, drained, rinsed (to get rid of the part that makes you gassy, which is not necessary with lentils), and then mixed in.

The chopped vegetables can either be added part-way through the onion-cooking, so that they're gently fried and then simmered along with everything else, or you can roast them in an oven and stir them in near the end. Alternatively, if using mostly root vegetables, you can boil or steam them, then add near the end.

Good vegetables for a spicy sauce include potatoes, peas, carrots, green beans, courgettes, aubergines, bell or sweet peppers, mushrooms, cauliflower, tomatoes and okra.

Herby tomato sauce

Make the sauce as above, but instead of aromatic spices like turmeric and cinnamon, add herbs like oregano, rosemary, basil and thyme near the end of cooking.

Butter beans, green lentils and puy lentils go really well with this kind of sauce. Balsamic vinegar and/or red wine can be added for extra depth.

Herby tomato sauce is great on pasta and pizzas, and as the base for ratatouille.

Stir-fry

A stir-fry is one of the quickest, cheapest, easiest and healthiest meals you can knock up. All you have to do is heat a small amount of vegetable or sesame oil in a wok at a high temperature, then chuck in baby sweetcorn, mangetout, and vegetables sliced into batons and sliced again so they are a few millimetres thick, such as carrots, sweet potatoes, red or yellow peppers, cabbage and courgettes. Spring onions can just be sliced lengthwise a few times. Turn regularly with a spatula. After a couple of minutes, add vegetables that cook faster, such as spring onions and broccoli. Give it another couple of minutes, turn the heat off, add seasonings, such as chilli sauce, minced garlic, pickled or grated ginger and soya sauce, and you're done.

A really nice topping is tahini and lemon sauce. If you want some protein, include cashew nuts in your stir-fry, or cubes of deep-fried tofu (available in bags from Chinese supermarkets.) Alternatively, cut a block of firm tofu into cubes, stir in a mix of soya sauce and olive oil, and bake in a medium oven for 20 minutes to give the cubes a chewy skin. These can be refrigerated for up to three days and used in stir-fries and a wide range of other dishes.

Béchamel (white) cheesy sauce

For tasty macaroni pasta, cauliflower cheese or lasagne, make a lovely white sauce. It's very easy. If you want it to taste really cheesy, see the tips on replacing cheese later in this chapter.

The basic principle is to gently fry a finely-chopped onion in some oil or vegan margarine, then, when it is soft and transparent, stir in plain flour, stirring until it forms a thick paste, called a roux. Continue to fry another couple of minutes and then slowly stir in soya milk until you have a thick sauce. If it's lumpy, blend. For the best flavour, cook on a very low heat for at least 20 minutes. A roux can also be made without onion, with just fat and flour.

Home-made pesto

Pesto transforms pasta into a full meal, and it's a great idea to have a jar in your fridge for times when you're in a hurry. Simply grind toasted pine nuts with Brazil nuts or walnuts, basil leaves, garlic, olive oil and a little salt and pepper. Then mix in olive oil until the texture is right. Stirring in a few yeast flakes adds extra cheesiness. Wild garlic makes amazing pesto, though it has a shelf life of only a few days.

Salad ideas

Salad shouldn't just be iceberg lettuce, tomatoes and cucumber rings – that's a garnish! For a great, nutritious salad that's a meal in its own right, choose a really dark-leaved, full flavoured lettuce, like Romaine (cos), little gem, lollo rosso or oakleaf. Slice thinly, arrange on a plate and pile on some other tasty leaves, like rocket or radicchio, plus grated carrot, sliced vine or cherry tomato, sliced avocado, sliced red, orange or yellow pepper, and cucumber sliced very thin.

Make a dressing from olive oil and lemon juice, with a little mustard or balsamic vinegar. Tahini with apple juice also makes a really good dressing.

Pulses (legumes)

Dried beans are cheap, full of protein and fibre, and extremely versatile.

It's best to soak beans overnight or at any rate for at least six hours, then drain to remove most of the oligosaccharides. These are large starch molecules in the outer layer of the bean that we cannot digest, but which bacteria in our large intestine can digest, resulting in the production of gas and farting.

Add three times the volume of fresh water to the soaked beans, bring to a boil, then simmer until soft. Each type of bean has a slightly different cooking time, ranging from about 30 to about 90 minutes. You can tell when they're done by squeezing a couple: if there's no hard, gritty bit in the middle, you're there. Throw away the cooking water, as it contains the last of the oligosaccharides. Red kidney beans are a special case, because they need to be boiled vigorously for at least ten minutes to destroy toxic lectins before you reduce the heat and let them simmer.

Lentils don't need to be soaked beforehand, and cook faster than beans.

Pulses MUST be cooked on their own and then added to vegetables, sauces, etc. near the end of cooking a dish. Otherwise, you could end up with some semi-raw ones hours later. It's also essential not to add any salt to the cooking water. A little bicarbonate of soda, however, will soften pulses. Some recipes for refried beans or mushy peas include it.

A pressure cooker drastically reduces the cooking time and is a worthwhile investment if you plan to use dried pulses regularly.

It's normal nowadays to buy tinned, cooked pulses, rinse and add to dishes. This is more expensive and not as environmentally-friendly, though it takes all the inconvenience out of cooking with pulses, especially if you prefer to cook one or two portions at a time.

Rice

Brown rice contains several times more fibre than white and a lot more flavour, though not everybody likes it at first. To cook long grain brown rice, add twice the volume of cold water to rice, boil, reduce heat to a simmer and cover with a lid, then turn off the heat when the water is absorbed, which takes about 20 minutes and you should not stir it at all until cooked. Then leave to sit and steam until needed. The rice will take on a slightly frayed look when done, so the edges don't look smooth anymore. White rice is cooked in the same way, though you can pretty much turn the heat off and let it sit as soon as the water comes to a boil.

Nuts

Nuts require very little cooking and are usually either lightly toasted or blanched when you buy them. Add to dishes near the end of the cooking time.

Portion sizes

Everybody's appetite is different and so it's hard to advise portion sizes. A general rule is that 100g of dry rice or pasta will make a large portion, 50g a side portion. 50g potatoes will make a small to medium portion, half an onion or half a tin of chickpeas per person and so on. It all depends what else will be in your meal and whether it will be the main meal of the day.

Cooking in bulk

To save time and money if you live alone, cook several portions of food in one go, allow to cool, decant into food bags or re-used takeaway tubs, hummus pots, glass tubs or jars, and freeze. Alternatively, take it in turns to cook for friends.

It's also a good idea to prepare versatile components of meals in bulk. For example, roast cubes of vegetables like courgettes, aubergines, red onions and squash, and then use in a variety of stews, salads, curry, pasta sauce, on top of couscous, etc.

CONVENIENCE FOODS FOR BUSY PEOPLE

It's easier than ever to live vegan at work, rest and play. Gone are the dark ages, when we had to cook everything from scratch, or settle for chips and yucky made-up things like nut cutlets. Nowadays a modern worker, student or busy parent can choose from a wide range of meals and ingredients from supermarkets, and throwing together a quick, tasty meal needn't mean missing out on nutrients.

Ready-to-eat microwavable rice, marinated tofu chunks and some tahini sauce in a squirty bottle means you can knock up a quick accompaniment to some stir-fried veg. Pile on the salted, roasted cashew nuts and add a tin of coconut milk for more protein and variety.

Vegan chilli can be bought in tins, as can a wide range of soups and tapas delights such as stuffed vine leaves. Pasta sauce often comes with capers instead of fish these days, and larger supermarkets stock cheese-free pesto that you can stir into pasta for a 10-minute meal.

The modern office worker spurns soggy sandwiches in favour of wraps, sushi, or a tub of couscous topped with roast veg cubes, that can be microwaved and eaten at their desk. Simply prepare a big tray of chunks of courgettes, aubergines, onions and other veg, then roast and store in your fridge for up to three days' worth of meals.

Chinese supermarkets stock more types of tofu than you ever thought possible, including bags of deep-fried chunks for texture and ease of cooking. In Chinese shops it's usually called beancurd. Check the freezer section for fake duck roast, chicken nuggets and even fake fish.

The smaller, city centre "Express" supermarkets are geared towards local workers, and they sell an increasing range of refrigerated one-pot noodle and rice dishes that you pop in a microwave. Bombay potatoes, onion bhajias, ready-made poppadoms and various types of curry can be combined with dairy-free yoghurt and chutney for an instant feast.

If you like your food basic and junky, you'll find that many brands of instant dried noodles are animal free, including some of the famous ones that come in pots.

Free-from aisles in supermarkets are worth a look, though a lot of the food there is geared towards gluten-free shoppers and it can be very pricey.

We've found that Indian takeaways are far more clued-up than they were before, with many having an online ordering service, where you can specify that they do your curry dairy-free. Look up a website, choose your dishes, add your comment and an email pings back in under ten minutes, telling you when your food will be ready to collect. You can place your order as you leave work and collect on your way home. What could be simpler? Well, getting it delivered by someone on a motorbike is easier, though you normally have to pay a large proportion of the sale price in delivery charges.

Independent sandwich shops and trading estate catering vans tend to be behind the times, with hardly any choice, though we've found that if you tell them you've just got a job nearby and will be a regular customer, they may bend over backwards to cater for you.

Chips are almost always cooked in vegetable oil everywhere outside Yorkshire, and busy takeaways usually have a separate fryer for their chips. Falafels are becoming more popular, with falafel salad bars springing up everywhere in large cities. They usually have long opening hours, and some have an entirely vegan menu.

Burrito bars can also be promising, with a mix of stir-fried veg, rice, beans, salsa, guacamole and jalapenos wrapped up in flatbread for a cheap, filling sit-in or takeway meal.

All chain restaurants and many independent ones have a presence on Facebook these days, and it's easier than ever to message or email comments and feedback about the kind of food you want.

If you're set on sandwiches, you'll find hummus, sun-dried tomatoes and olives all over the place, plus olive tapenade, artichoke hearts in jars, and vegan sausages that you can eat from the pack. Try health food shops for mushroom and vegetable patés, egg-free mayonnaise and ham-style slices.

A typical working week's midday meals could look like this:

- Monday: Vegan sausage roll with mixed leaf salad, three bean salad and hummus.

- Tuesday: Home-made or takeaway sandwich with olives, stuffed vine leaves and crisps.

- Wednesday: Chips with mushy peas and brown sauce.

- Thursday: Couscous, roast vegetables and chickpeas, made at home and re-heated in office microwave. Served with soya sauce and tahini sauce.

- Friday: Noodle pot with tofu cubes. A thick banana and berry smoothie.

REPLACING MEAT

There are two ways that you can replace meat in your favourite dishes. Either use wholefoods and vegetables that have a slightly meaty taste and texture, or opt for a meat substitute.

Puy lentils, green lentils, aubergines, mushrooms, marinated or smoked tofu, tempeh, chickpeas, miso, cashew nuts and chestnuts can all make very effective meat substitutes, depending on the recipe. Here are some suggestions for dishes to try them in.

- Lasagne or moussaka – Puy lentils or frozen soya mince instead of mince. Also use plenty of aubergine.
- Tuna salad – Steamed, grated tempeh in mayonnaise instead of tuna.
- Curry – Use chick peas.
- Duck – Mock duck, available in tins from Chinese supermarkets.
- Sandwiches – There's a whole range of ham and sausage style slices available, plus smoked or marinated and baked tofu works really well.
- Kebabs on a barbecue – Vegan sausages, tofu, tempeh or seitan-based steak.
- Oxtail soup – Miso soup.
- Sausage casserole – Vegan sausages. Or use mushrooms.
- Thai Coconut Curry – Cashew nuts and deep-fried cubes of tofu.
- Haggis – The vegan ones now sell better than the meat ones.
- Cooked breakfast – Use sosmix or pre-made vegan sausages, scrambled tofu or one of the powdered, seaweed-based egg substitutes, proper vegan black pudding from Lancashire, seitan or soya-based rashers, or smoked tempeh, potato cakes and baked beans. Plus toast and fried or grilled tomatoes, of course. Add mushrooms, if you must, but please not if Ronny's coming to breakfast.

REPLACING CHEESE

Cheese is often the thing that people struggle to give up the most. It is usually the flavour rather than texture of cheese people miss, plus the fact that it is usually 'the vegetarian option' that old-fashioned caterers use for sandwiches etc, so vegetarians tend to get used to eating it. Back in the early 1990s when the authors cut animal products out of our diets, we had to do all kinds of strange things to replace cheese, such as frying up onions with soya flour and yeast extract. This made a substance with the texture of putty, which cleaved its way down your throat and seemed to suck all of the moisture out of your mouth!

Thankfully, times have changed. Wholefood shops, along with some delis and supermarkets, stock several types of vegan cheese and they all have slightly different flavours and textures. Here's a summary:

Coconut-oil based

The most common and versatile type. Cheap, melts well and comes in a variety of flavours.

Soya-based

The long-established option that's been around since the 1990s. The solid ones don't melt very well and have largely been phased out, though the creamy spreads are as popular as ever.

Fermented nut based

The most authentically cheesy flavours and also the most expensive. Fermented cheeses are typically made from cashews, almonds, or sunflower seeds, and regarded as artisan products. They're increasingly in demand. They tend to be stocked by small, independent retailers, rather than supermarkets.

Potato or pea starch based

These were an early alternative to soya-based cheeses. They can still be found in some shops and are surprisingly nice.

Making your own cheese sauce

Cheese has a sharp, sweet, salty, sour and yeasty flavour. We can replicate it in a cheese sauce that can be used everywhere such as in lasagne, on top of chilli, put blobs of it on a pizza, or spread on toast.

First make the béchamel sauce according to the directions in the Kitchen Techniques section earlier in this chapter. Now make it cheesy! Cheese tastes sharp, sweet, sour and salty, with a base note of yeasty, fermented earthiness. Stir in about a teaspoon of each of these: (SHARP) mustard, (SWEET) sugar or concentrated apple juice (or use sweetened soya milk in the first place), (SOUR) lemon juice or vinegar, (SALTY) soya sauce or tomato puree, and finally (YEASTY) Engevita yeast flakes, or yeast extract. Play around with these to suit your own taste.

For lots of vegan cheese recipes and "uncheese" dishes get
The Ultimate Uncheese Cookbook by Joanne Stepaniak.

Parmesan

Shop-bought Parmesan can never be vegetarian, let alone vegan.
If you want a strong-flavoured cheese to sprinkle on your pizzas
and pasta, try grinding up lightly-toasted Brazil or cashew nuts
and mixing with some sea salt and *Engevita* nutritional yeast
flakes. You'll be pleasantly surprised how nice it is.

REPLACING BUTTER, YOGURT AND OTHER ANIMAL MILK PRODUCTS

Recipes often state "vegan butter", which can be confusing.
Many cooks replace butter with coconut oil in recipes, as it
is solid at room temperature.

Vegetable spreads, such as *Flora* and *Vitalite*, and now even spreads
called vegan butter, are good for all kinds of situations in which
you may have used butter before, such as spreading on toast, and
making pastry with, hence many of us now have a tub in our fridge.

Vegetable spreads used to be called "margarine" until fairly
recently, and many recipes still refer to margarine, or marg. The
food industry moved away from using this term, as margarine
used to be made with vegetable oil that had been hydrogenated to
make it solid at room temperature. Hydrogenated fats are a type
of trans fat that does not occur in nature, and these were found to
significantly raise blood cholesterol in people who ate them regularly.
Due to all the negative publicity linking trans fats with heart disease,
manufacturers switched to palm oil, which is naturally solid at
room temperature and has virtually no flavour, and blended this
with other oils, such as sunflower, or rapeseed.

Some people boycott palm oil for environmental reasons unless
they know it has been harvested sustainably, and even then some
people will not touch it. At the time of writing, there is one palm-oil
free brand, called *Naturli*, that is available from UK wholefood
shops and rarely seen in supermarkets.

In baking you can replace butter by vegan butter or rapeseed oil or
sunflower oil. You can now get solid vegetable fat from supermarket

fridges that is packaged like butter and tastes very similar. It isn't a spread, it's plant-based butter.

Olive oil can replace butter very effectively in many recipes, and is ideal for making garlic bread. Unlike most other oils, olive oil has a rich, earthy, complex flavour, that gives most dishes a luxury feel in the same kind of way that butter does.

All supermarkets and health food shops now stock vegan yogurt, which is typically made from soya, although coconut and almond milk versions also exist. Some stock it alongside dairy yogurt, whereas others have a specific "Free From" fridge. Vegan yogurt comes in natural unsweetened, as well as a wide variety of fruity flavours. We've recently seen vegan Greek-style and high-protein versions too.

In baking replace dairy milk by almond or soya or oat milk.

REPLACING EGGS

When making a vegan full British cooked breakfast, scrambled eggs have traditionally been replaced by scrambled tofu (soft or firm) crumbled, adding for example *Engevita* yeast flakes, a pinch of *kala namak* black salt or celery salt, tamari soya sauce, and also a little bit of turmeric, which makes it yellow. Some black pepper works well in it too.

Leftover scramble can be reheated or used in Chinese style stir-fry rice or sandwiches.

One of the things that confuses new vegans the most is how to replace eggs in baked goods such as cakes. Here are your options.

Replace one egg with:

Ground flax seeds: 1 tablespoon combined with 3 tablespoons water, leave for 5 to 10 minutes until it thickens. This is good for situations where you need a sticky substance that helps things bind together such as gluten-free baking.

In many sponge cake recipes, simply use slightly more baking powder.

Banana: Half a large or one medium ripe banana mashed. A banana adds texture as well as stickiness to a recipe and also makes the batter denser and with a tinge of banana taste. This works really well in American style thick pancakes, some cookies and loaf tin style cakes.

Tofu: This is similar to cooked egg white and good for dishes that involve a lot of egg white such as quiche, egg salad, or ice cream. Use a piece about the size of an egg to replace one egg.

Aquafaba: is Latin for bean water, in particular from a can of chickpeas. It replaces egg white in two ways. One is to whisk it until firm to replace egg white in situations like meringues and very light cake batter such as a yule log, which needs to be light so you can roll it. The other use is where you want to coat or glaze something, for example katsu curry or tofish, when you are coating with breadcrumbs before frying. For example coat a piece of tofu or tempeh in flour, then aquafaba instead of egg white, then breadcrumbs (panko breadcrumbs for katsu curry), and deep fry it. Use about 2 tbs for one egg white.

Gram (chickpea) flour: in small quantities can add a slightly eggy flavour and more stickiness to some recipes such as French toast.

Egg replacer powder: comes in two versions. The old-fashioned sort is a blend of starches that is good for cookies, muffins, cakes etc. Just follow the suggestions on the packet. The other type is more modern, seaweed based and quite nutritious. It has an eggy texture and can be cooked on its own instead of scrambled egg.

Cornstarch: 2 tbs with 3 tbs water, is perfect for making custard. Mix well and pour into heated soya or other plant milk. Keep stirring and heating until thick enough.

Some old-fashioned vegetarian recipes such as nut roast call for egg as a binder, which can be replaced by tahini or nut butter, 3 tablespoons for one egg. Or add some oats to the recipe.

Carbonated mineral water: 60ml instead of an egg, can be used with commercial packet cake mixes.

When baking gluten-free cakes, pies, pizza bases and pastry, it's a good idea to add a little xanthan gum. This helps to keep things moist, as gluten-free baked goods tend to dry out when they cool down.

For some of Ronny's vegan baking recipes get yourself a copy of *The Return of The Cake Scoffer* from this publisher's website.

HOW TO EAT FOR LITTLE MORE THAN A POUND A DAY

Yes, it's possible. The authors have done it during desperate times, and know people who still live this way, short term. The basic principle is to completely re-think how you see food, by assessing all purchases in terms of how filling and nutritious they are. Eating out isn't an option, and neither are takeaways. Processed foods such as vegan sausages and chocolate bars will take you over budget, as will alcohol, olives, coffee, fruit, and most salad ingredients.

Start off by buying things like rice, pasta, lentils, oats, dried pulses, sugar, tea bags, oil and flour in bulk. Never buy tinned beans or chickpeas, as they cost over three times more. Use dried ones, soak the amount you need overnight, and boil as needed. Alternatively, cook large quantities and freeze in portion-sized bags, as this saves time and fuel.

Have a think about the vegetables you like the most and use these as your staple ingredients, always having them in your cupboard. Frozen vegetables can be cheaper than you think, with large bags of peas and sweetcorn costing typically £1 at the time of writing. A bag of frozen peas can last you a week and go in all sorts of dishes, from curry to stew. Potatoes, onions and carrots are good staple foods that are very versatile. Apples are the most affordable fruit and they also have a relatively long shelf life.

Only buy vegetables you hardly use if you have a specific meal in mind, such as an aubergine to go in ratatouille. If you just buy a vegetable for the sake of more variety, you'll end up throwing some of it out. The number one rule of eating on a tight budget is that you must never throw anything away, so meals must be planned before you shop, unless you're the sort who'll happily eat the same thing for days on end.

Tea bags, noodles, bread and jam can all be bought for bargain prices in small quantities. Tinned tomatoes work out much cheaper than fresh, and studies have shown that the vitamin content is just as high.

Stock up on spices, rice, oil, etc. at a Chinese or Indian cash & carry, as although the initial outlay will be higher, you'll save lots of money over time. If there isn't one near you, Asian supermarkets tend to have many bulk items and are almost as cheap. If you live in a village or a small rural town with a mainly white population, you'll have to travel to the nearest city, which could take you well over budget.

Cook lots of food at once, especially things like curry. Then freeze in meal-sized portions and re-heat as you need them. Have a mutual exchange with a friend, where you take it in turns to cook for each other.

Supermarkets are the cheapest option for things like pasta, toilet roll, alcohol and washing powder, yet surprisingly expensive for vegetables and fresh herbs, with the exception of Aldi and Lidl. Veg can typically cost twice as much from a supermarket as a market stall, and tofu can be an eye-watering four times as much as from a Chinese supermarket. The cheapest place for vegetables is outdoor market stalls, closely followed by indoor markets. It's common for stallholders to put large bowls or scoops of bananas, tomatoes and other perishable foods out at the front of the stall as they are starting to pack away and yell "Pound a scoop", so it's worth getting there late afternoon. You can get some veg for free if you go after trading has finished and don't mind picking things up off the ground. Sometimes you'll have rich pickings, while other days you'll only find cauliflower leaves and squashed tomatoes.

Wholefood shops operate with higher overheads than supermarkets and cannot afford to offer big discounts in the same way. Some shops will let you order items in bulk through them, so it's worth asking.

Go to supermarkets an hour or two before closing for reduced-price perishable items like bread and salad vegetables. Another top tip for eating cheaply is, if you see bargain price short dated soft fruit, such as strawberries, grapes or blueberries, buy the whole lot, then cut any stalks or leaves off and freeze in bags or tubs. They can be used for smoothies, with porridge, or just eat a handful for a snack.

If you have a sunny windowsill, grow your own fresh herbs and salad leaves in small pots and seed trays.

A typical day's meals could include:

- Breakfast: Mug of tea with bowl of porridge.

- Dinner: Pasta with tomato and chilli sauce

- Mid afternoon snack: Tea and toast with a few biscuits. A banana.

- Evening meal: Tomato and lentil curry with rice

There's another way to eat for very little money, and that is to forage some or all of your food from the large bins on wheels around the back of supermarkets and other shops. This is called "skipping" in Britain, and "dumpster diving" in most other countries. This foraging can be interpreted as stealing by some shop staff, so it involves being intrepid and planning carefully. Some of our friends have done it for years, and it makes ecological sense, as thousands of tonnes of perfectly edible food are thrown away every year. Typical things that you can find in skips include bread, soft fruit, tomatoes and mushrooms. There are lively discussion groups on social media, where you can pick up tips and learn from more experienced people.

How to eat on five pounds a day

On five pounds a day, you can expand on the limited diet above, to afford things like coffee, veggie sausage and burger mix, soya chunks, tinned pulses, baked beans, creamed coconut, nuts and seeds, fresh herbs, salad leaves, fruit and occasional takeaway treats such as chips. You still have to be careful to limit your intake of processed foods though, and luxury things like chocolate and margarine are only affordable if you go for the cheapest supermarket basic brands. You won't be able to afford soya milk and tofu from health food shops, and should still be careful to avoid any impulse spending. If you want beer, wine or cider, get a homebrew kit.

Top tips for eating cheaply:

- Base your diet on rice, bread and pulses, with fried onions, dried herbs, spices and oils for flavour and texture. Half the world's population eat this way, so it isn't as weird as you think. Porridge makes a bargain-price, very nutritious breakfast.

- Tinned tomatoes or passata (sieved tomatoes in cartons) can be used as the base for curries and pasta sauces.

- Fruit is surprisingly expensive, so weigh up how filling and nutritious an item of fruit is before buying. Apples and bananas usually work out cheapest, though it all depends on the time of year and whether there are special offers on.

- Potatoes, carrots and onions are usually the cheapest vegetables, and they all have a good shelf life.

- Frozen vegetables like peas and sweetcorn are worth getting from supermarkets as they can work out very economical.

- Plan your meals. Never buy anything on impulse.
  Everything you buy must be eaten.

- Cook in bulk if you can store meal-sized portions, or take
  it in turns to have other skint friends round for dinner.

- You won't be able to afford health food shops, and will almost
  certainly have to compromise your ethics on things like Fairtrade.

- Chocolate, berries, coffee, alcohol and salad leaves should be seen
  as luxuries, to be avoided or indulged in occasionally. You can
  grow your own salad leaves easily on a windowsill for a few pence.

- Free food can be salvaged from skips, or picked up around
  vacant market stalls after trading has finished.

How to eat on a high budget

Not everyone with a vegan lifestyle is on a tight budget! If you're a
successful rock star, or you've just won a large wedge of cash, there
are plenty of vegan ways to spend it.

Raw food catalogues are full of ingredients and supplements that will
set you back hundreds of pounds without much effort, and there's a
range of amazing juicers, blenders and other kitchen equipment that
can turn your kitchen into a food laboratory. They also sell items like
raw chocolate, "superfoods" such as lucuma and maca, and flax crackers
in small quantities that easily work out at over £30 a kilo, so stock up.

Alas, vegetarian and vegan restaurants are all remarkably good
value compared to mainstream places, as well as having way better
food. You might be able to spend £50-£60 on food at a top place, so
even with drinks you'll barely match the price of an upper mid-range
mainstream restaurant.

A better bet is to head for a posh hotel with top-end chefs, where a
three course meal or seven course tasting menu could relieve your
pocket of another hundred pounds, and that's before you get to the
wine list. Although vegan options on such menus are likely to be sparse,
you'll probably find that they'll want your money enough to bend
over backwards for you. Pop-up restaurants and supper clubs are a
fashionable option these days, and also tend to be fairly expensive.

A recent development is companies who send you boxes of vegan meals, mail order. These are good quality meals, cooked by chefs in a central kitchen and flash frozen, then couriered to your door, vacuum-packed. People typically buy a week's worth of meals at a time. It's a high quality and much healthier alternative to takeaways, which is far more expensive than buying the ingredients and cooking them yourself.

EATING OUTSIDE

Here are some easy ideas for meals to take to work or school, or lunch in the park.

Meals to carry in a lunch box

Salad with avocado and falafel, or beans or lentils, or marinated or smoked tofu pieces. Vegetable spring rolls, samosas and onion bhajias with dipping sauce. Sandwiches, wraps, pasties, sushi and soya sausage rolls.

If you can reheat food at work

Last night's leftovers.
Canned or home made soup.
Or try a shop-bought ready meal such as Indian food with rice, from supermarkets or health food shops.
Baked potato, with baked beans or chilli, and salad.

Sandwiches

Vegan cheese or meat or paté with crunchy salad, chutney or pickle. Rice cakes or oatcakes make a convenient and more compact alternative to bread.

Food to buy

Light meals and snacks can be bought from many cafes, shops and takeaways on the way to work, or pop out during your break. Many cafes offer milkshakes and smoothies made with plant milks. The options are constantly changing and improving as chain shops and restaurants add more and more vegan options, such as vegan cheese on pizzas, falafels, fake meats, salad bars, plus grab-and-go food in the fridge.

Happy Cow, a website and free app, displays a local map of most cities in the world with vegan (green), vegetarian (purple) and omnivorous (red) cafes and restaurants recommended by vegan travellers and locals. Click on a place for more details.

Snacks from shops

Health food stores are great for stocking up on cereal and raw food bars and flapjacks, plus more exciting things like dairy-free chocolate coated raisins, marshmallows and fudge. Big supermarkets and sweet shops are catching on to demand and stocking things like this nowadays, especially in urban, multicultural areas, and busy streets full of office workers. Many are labelled vegan, otherwise you will need to check the ingredients.

Ready salted (plain) crisps are always vegan. Certain brands have other vegan flavours, such as "prawn cocktail" and salt and vinegar, that are clearly labelled. Watch out for lurking lactose and whey in unexpected places, plus some of the more luxury crisps have actual powdered meat in flavours like bacon and sausage.

Many large supermarkets stock soya, and possibly coconut or almond, yogurts in various flavours. Vegan biscuits are available in all supermarkets, either in the biscuit aisle or the Free From section. In the UK for example, bourbons and ginger nuts are usually vegan, but check the ingredients to make sure.

The original vegan portable snack, of course, is fresh fruit, raisins, dried fruit, nuts or seeds.

RONNY'S READS

There are new vegan cookbooks published every year, to suit every taste and budget. Here are Ronny's recommendations.

BOSH! by Henry Firth and Ian Theasby: It's only two years old, yet it's the biggest-selling vegan cookbook on Amazon. Hats off to these guys, for helping turn vegan food mainstream. They've since written *Speedy BOSH!* and *BISH BASH BOSH!*

Dirty Vegan by Matt Pritchard: A really cool cookbook full of photos, by a TV presenter. If you like tattoos, skateboards and urban graffiti, you'll want this on your coffee table.

Plants-only Kitchen by Gaz Oakley: Wholefoods, millennial-style. Gaz Oakley creates healthy food for busy people with small kitchens.

15 Minute Vegan by Katy Beskow: This does what it says on the tin. Simple, foolproof recipes, using everyday supermarket ingredients. A great-value introduction to vegan cooking.

Vegan One Pound Meals by Miguel Barclay: This London-based chef spotted a niche. Attractive, modern recipes that cost under £1 a portion. His first few books were bestsellers, so he created an all-vegan one.

Vegan Mock Meat Revolution by Jackie Kearney: BBC's *Masterchef* finalist created a book of vegan meat-replacement meals and snacks. Recommended by Animal Aid and PETA.

Ms Cupcake – The Naughtiest Vegan Cakes in Town! by Mellissa Morgan: All the vegan cake recipes you could possibly want. A lovely-looking book, that makes an ideal gift.

Easy Vegan Cooking by Leah Leneman: This book is old-school, published in 1998 and still selling strong. Over 350 recipes makes it amazing value for money.

Rose Elliot's Complete Vegan by Rose Elliot: Rose has churned out solid, no-nonsense meat-free cookbooks since the 1980s. This recent one is possibly her best.

Veganomicon, 10th Anniversary Edition by Isa Moscowitz and Terry Romero: These vegan chefs have collaborated for decades to bring us top-notch, healthy comfort food. Isa also runs the recipe website The PPK.

Ageless Vegan by Tracye McQuirter: Mother and daughter cooks share vegan recipes and health tips that will help you stay young and vibrant.

Another Dinner is Possible – More Than Just a Vegan Cookbook by Mike and Isy: Brighton-based eco-activists produced a spiral-bound hardback book of wholefood recipes that gained rave reviews all around the world for its quality, value and fun tone. This 2016 (third) edition is hard to find in the shops, though you can get it from Active Distribution and ebay.

No Meat Athlete by Matt Frazier: A brilliant book if you want to run your personal best, plant-based. Recipes, training tips and motivational stories.

Eat and Run by Scott Jurek: Long-term plant-based ultrarunner shares his adventures and recipes in a book that's inspired runners all around the world to go vegan.

Ronny's recommended vegan cookery websites

Finding Vegan findingvegan.com
A multi-user site for recipe sharing. Most of the recipes link to the chefs' blogs, so this is a good starting point.

BBC Good Food bbcgoodfood.com/recipes/collection/vegan-recipes
All their vegan dishes compiled under one handy menu. Recipes are rated and reviewed by users, so you can spot which are popular.

Deliciously Ella deliciouslyella.com
Wholefood entrepreneur famous for her range of vegan snacks and breakfast cereals. Her beautiful and inspiring website has hundreds of great recipes.

Post Punk Kitchen theppk.com
A long-running American website that Ronny often refers to.

The Minimalist Baker minimalistbaker.com
Very reliable, straightforward recipes, Especially good for gluten-free cakes and bread.

Jamie Oliver jamieoliver.com/recipes/category/special-diets/vegan
This TV chef loves to promote vegetables, and he's always catered well for us. He's compiled all his vegan recipes and videos here. Also tips on things like Christmas dinner, making vegan gravy, and advice for other chefs about what we do and don't eat.

The Full Helping thefullhelping.com
Hearty, wholefood recipes by an American dietitian. Great if you're after high fibre, low-sugar, low-fat dishes.

The Veg Space thevegspace.co.uk
A nicely-designed site that groups dishes into starters, mains, pasta, soups etc. A site to bookmark and keep going back to.

HOLIDAYS

Travelling vegan can be easy, with a little preparation. Prepare well, travel easy, and feast. Don't prepare, travel hard, and end up eating "vegan by omission." Here's how to prepare for a tasty trip.

Travelling in the UK

Britain has vegan restaurants and even pubs up and down the country. Major chain restaurants and many independents nowadays also appreciate that attracting vegans, *and hence all the other people in their group*, is good for business. Add to that all the restaurants from countries where much of the food is naturally vegan, such as Indian, Lebanese or Turkish. Just stay away from French restaurants.

For an easy breakfast, and possibly dinner, there are over a hundred vegetarian or vegan bed & breakfasts around Britain. They tend to be concentrated in touristy areas such as Cornwall, Devon, Cumbria, Yorkshire, Scotland and Wales. You can find them in adverts at the back of vegan and vegetarian magazines and online.

When staying in cities, many hotels and guest houses these days can do you a vegan full English cooked breakfast. If not, then you could be putting orange juice on your breakfast cereal, unless you've asked them to get in some soya milk or brought your own. Be sure they understand that you are vegan, not vegetarian, and check the ingredients of any meat substitutes such as Quorn, which sometimes contains egg. Of course the simplest solution is to go Airbnb and have your own kitchen. **Vegvisits** is a vegetarian version of Airbnb and some of the hosts are vegan.

Happy Cow is a fantastic website and free app for vegans travelling almost anywhere in the world. It's a directory of vegetarian and vegan restaurants arranged by country and city. Enter your destination, and a map pops up covered by an overwhelming number of coloured icons. Zoom in and turn off everything except the first two, or three if you

want more options:
- Green: vegan
- Purple: vegetarian
- Red: omnivorous with vegan options
- Yellow: health food shops

Most cities and some other areas have a local Facebook vegan social group, possibly more than one. People on these love discussing their favourite places to eat out vegan. Find them on Facebook, or possibly meetup.com if you'd like to meet some locals. You may have to join first, then post a query such as "I'm coming to Manchester next week, staying in Chorlton, and will be spending time in the centre. Where is good to get vegan food?" You will receive lots of recommendations, and you may even get invited to a vegan meal with the local group. Also scroll back through the last few months of postings to see locals discussing favourite places to eat and new discoveries.

A fabulous time to visit a town is when a vegan festival or fayre or market is on. There are around 200 vegan festivals all over the UK each year, with new ones popping up all the time. These are usually in the city centre on a Saturday and/or Sunday, and can have over 100 vegan stalls, caterers, and free talks and cookery demonstrations.

Travelling abroad

When flying long haul, be sure to book a vegan meal with the code VGML. Confirm this with your travel agent, as it is easy to get mistakenly allocated a vegetarian meal, which has a different code. As you enter the plane, tell the flight attendants greeting you at the door that you have reserved a VGML vegan meal for seat 25C and please don't give it to a vegetarian by mistake, before the trolley reaches you.

Google places before you go, for example "vegan Prague", and settle in to read blog postings by vegan travellers. There are lots of vegan travel blogs and these can be a fabulous resource. Some have only a few suggestions and may be years old, but others can have ten or more recent detailed reviews with food photos, and you may even find articles by English speakers who actually live in the area.

The very best resource of all is a local guide compiled and kept up to date by vegans who live in the city or country. You can find a list of recommended sites on the links page at veganguides.uk.

Another possibility is to search for vegan groups on Facebook that post in English, which are surprisingly common as there can be a lot of English speakers living in any city. If you speak the local language or one that is related (e.g. Spanish, Portuguese and Italian are easy to read for speakers of any one of these) then find the Facebook vegan pages in that language, look back through them for restaurant discussions, post your own enquiry and make some local vegan friends. Local vegans will often be delighted to have the chance to practise their English.

As in the UK (above), Happy Cow, Airbnb and Vegvisits are great resources for vegans.

What about away from the cities? When eating in non-vegetarian places where staff have limited or no English, such as beachside restaurants in Thailand, you need the ***Vegan Passport.*** This is a passport-sized little book, road-tested by thousands of travelling vegans, and has a page for each of 79 languages explaining what vegans eat, including important details like no fish or chicken stock in my soup please. Give your *Vegan Passport* to your server and ask them to take it to the kitchen, and you will get a perfect vegan meal every time, without tuna on the salad, egg in the mayonnaise, or a bone at the bottom of your soup. It's published by the Vegan Society and available from the Vegetarian Guides website. There is also an app version.

Vegan travel companies

Yoga holidays are almost always at least vegetarian.
Find them in yoga magazines and online.

Here are some 100% vegan travel companies and vegan travel experts for all budgets:

- Green Earth Travel
- The Nomadic Vegan
- The Vegan Word
- Vegan Campout
- Vegan Cruises
- Vegan Culinary Cruises
- Vegan Epicure Travel

- Vegan Travel Club

- Vegan Guides Ltd (veganguides.eu)

- Veg Voyages

Further vegan travel reading

Caitlin Galer-Unti, founder of *The Vegan Word* travel website, has published two vegan travel books, available in paperback and ebook on amazon. ***Barcelona Vegan Guide*** covers the seaside city she has made home. ***The Essential Vegan Travel Guide*** shows how to find vegan food anywhere in the world, accommodation, travelling with children or a dog, connecting with local vegans, making food in your room, and best places to visit as a vegan.

CHAPTER 4
Vegan Tribes

If you spend time on social media, surfing forums or reading blogs with a vegan focus, you'll come across groups of people whose shared values give them a sense of community, and sometimes one-upmanship. A talk on a particular subject at a vegan festival will draw them together. We can playfully call them tribes.

Most of these tribe members are friendly, relaxed and open minded, whereas a handful can be confrontational in asserting that theirs is the only way to be a "true" vegan.

Here's a rundown of some common vegan tribes.

Animal Activists

Many people cite animal suffering as their sole concern, and for them being vegan is purely about opting out of paying for animals to be enslaved in farms. They aren't necessarily environmentally aware or interested in healthy living. These tribe members tend to be very dedicated to their vegan lifestyle long-term, often boycotting companies with any involvement in animal farming or testing, or even refusing to listen to music or watch films made by celebrities who go hunting. This altruism can easily lead to anger and self-righteousness and you'll find a lot of arguments about that online. Most animal activists stay vegan for life and are very consistent in their views and shopping choices. The more friendly, self-aware ones share a strong sense of solidarity. Some only make friends with other activists, as they struggle too much to be around people who don't put animals at the centre of everything. Others start off purely as animal activists though broaden their horizons to include environmental and social justice considerations in almost everything they do.

Most likely to say: "Human freedom, animal rights. One struggle, one fight."

Least likely to say: "I buy the cheapest brands and hope they're not animal tested."

Animal Rescuers

Some animal activists conclude that the best way to help animals is to fill their homes with them, and they become carers to a wide range of refugees from the pet and farming industries.

The biggest dilemma these tribe members have is whether to feed cats on meat. Some insist that buying meat for cats makes no sense at all as it requires killing many animals to feed one, while others argue that cats are "obligate carnivores" and that feeding them a vegan diet is too risky. (See chapter 5 for an animal rights vet's verdict on the reality.)

Most likely to say: "Don't breed and buy while stray dogs die."

Least likely to say: "Let's go to Crufts dog show and see which breed wins Best in Show."

Baketivists

During the 1990s, vegan cake and pudding fans got sick and tired of getting served up sugar-free date slice, sorbets and fruit salads as the vegan dessert option. The only vegan cake recipes in cookbooks were dry, chewy affairs, based on wholemeal flour. Vegan cake lovers rose up! Ronny published *The Cake Scoffer* in 2000, and an explosion of other baking booklets followed, many with cute cartoons and colour pictures. The baking revolution began, as evangelical sweet-toothed cooks spread the Good Word of vegan cake.

Nowadays you'll find glossy hardback cookbooks with tempting photos, vegan cake cafes such as Cookies & Scream or Vida Bakery in London, craft bakers earning a living from home, and hundreds of cake and biscuit baking recipe blogs, filled with stylish fonts and photographs of beautiful food.

Most likely to say: "I've just made the most amazing rhubarb and custard cupcakes, using amaranth flour and vanilla dust."

Least likely to say: "Wholemeal date slices rock my world."

Convenience Food Fans

Food isn't just fuel, it appeals directly to our emotions. Those who grew up eating a fried breakfast every Sunday around a table with their family can subconsciously trigger happy memories, simply by devouring a fat vegan fry-up. A kebab at 2a.m. after a wild night out can be very satisfying, so what's wrong with a vegan kebab? It does the job, the same way as a meat one.

Some people base their vegan diet on convenience foods and takeaways, dodging fresh salads and the chore of cooking. These people tend not to make any claims that their diet is particularly healthy due to the high fat and salt content, and it certainly isn't cheap to live this way, though it saves loads of time. Convenience food lovers can get very excited on internet forums every time a new brand of vegan sausage, milkshake or pie hits the shops.

A typical day's meals could be vegan sausages, scrambled tofu and beans on toast for breakfast, followed by a defrosted vegan ham and pineapple pizza with chips for the midday meal, and curry and rice from a takeaway in the evening. Those who seek a more nutritionally complete diet tend to snack on fruit, as after all, fruit is the ultimate convenience food!

Most likely to say: "Where can I get a vegan pie and ice cream sundae, in Norwich, on a Sunday?"

Least likely to say: "I'm going raw."

Eco-Activists

Animal farming of all kinds is the most environmentally destructive activity on our planet, bar none. Eco-activists cite livestock farming as a massive waste of energy and land, as up to ten times more people could be fed on a plant-based diet. When you consider the polluting effects of animal slurry and also the additional energy required to process and store meat, milk and fish, the environmental argument makes absolute sense, and it's no wonder that so many people go vegan as a sustainable alternative.

Some eco-activists reject the concept of animal rights and some have no interest at all in fitness or diet. Some become freegan (eating whatever they can find), as they don't have an aversion to eating animal products, only to funding planet-trashing farming. Many also reject non-organic and highly processed food, or products that have been transported halfway around the world, like Brazil nuts.

Palm oil is a fashionable target for environmental activists, with many trying to have a diet free from this ingredient. This poses problems when buying processed vegan food, as palm oil is conveniently solid (saturated) at room temperature and is almost universally used in vegan margarine and pastries as a healthier alternative to hydrogenated vegetable fat. Online vegan forums can quickly become heated on this subject, with opponents claiming that palm oil is "not vegan", even though the same deforestation argument applies to sugar cane, coffee and soya.

Most likely to say: "I'm not going there, they use plastic packaging."

Least likely to say: "Let's go on a budget flight to Greece for the weekend."

Fitness Junkies

Many athletes and bodybuilders go vegan, including tennis players, snooker champions, boxers, runners and triathletes. Some ethical vegans get into fitness as a way to smash the stereotype that they are pale, skinny weaklings, then realise how much they love looking and feeling toned, buff and full of energy. You'll find thriving vegan fitness communities online, with a strong ethos of friendly peer support. Sportsmen and women with a plant-based diet who compete at an international level get promoted and celebrated a lot by this tribe.

Athletes and bodybuilders have very different diets, with athletes relying on lots of carbohydrates and wholefoods, and bodybuilders bulking up with protein and convenience foods.

Most likely to say: "I ran my personal best, and have epic, balls-to-the-wall lifting sessions on a vegan diet."

Least likely to say: "I'm a couch potato.

Foodies

Some vegan chefs aren't satisfied with rice and curry slop; they want to push the boundaries and become kitchen scientists. In the hands of this small but growing tribe of geniuses, food is transformed into works of art. Foodies will try daring combinations of ingredients, such as banana peel, herbs in custard, or pomegranate seeds in salads. In fact, by the time this goes to print, pomegranate seeds will probably be old-hat and sun-dried tomatoes may have even made a comeback. Foodies will shop online for rare dried mushrooms or spices, and will travel far to check out a new vegan-friendly restaurant with a five-course tasting menu. Nothing winds a foodie up more than the suggestion that the vegan diet is restrictive and bland.

An internet search will bring up some inspiring vegan foodie blogs, with stunning photography.

Most likely to say: "I just tried marinating Bolivian field mushrooms in red wine reduction with chocolate thyme sprigs and grapefruit foam."

Least likely to say: "I live on chips and beans."

Food Not Bombs and People's Kitchen

Food Not Bombs is an all-volunteer global movement that shares free vegan meals as a protest against war and poverty. Food Not Bombs groups collect surplus food that would otherwise go to waste from grocery stores, bakeries and markets, as well as donations from local farmers, then prepare community meals which are served for free to anyone who is hungry, typically from a pasting table in the street. The movement started in America in the 1980s, though there are a few groups in Britain.

People's Kitchens are similar to Food Not Bombs. They are events typically held in the evenings in community centres, at which a nutritious and imaginative vegan meal is served up for donations. The menu is usually family-friendly and allergy-aware.

Most likely to say: "I'm bidding on a 60 litre stockpot on ebay."

Least likely to say: "We're aiming for a Michelin star."

Foragers

A very nutritious way to supplement a low-cost diet is foraging. Fruit, nuts, seeds, nettles, sorrel, wild garlic, clover and dandelions are well known foods for free. However, you might be amazed by the full list of flowers, leaves and mushrooms that are edible. There are some great foraging books out there, to make sure you don't poison yourself!

Most likely to say: "I just foraged a sackload of blackberries on the common."

Least likely to say: "I never much cared for greens."

Gleegans (gluten-free vegans)

Gluten is a kind of stretchy protein found in many grassy cereal grains and products that contain them. This includes wheat, spelt, rye, barley, couscous, bulgur, triticale and some oats. It also includes processed foods that contain them, including most TVP chunks and brands of beer, most brands of vegan sausages and burgers, seitan (processed wheat gluten, used a lot in American recipes and increasingly in cafés), oat milk and most types of soya sauce.

Some people avoid gluten because it makes them feel bloated, whereas others have coeliac disease, which is a serious auto-immune condition that can cause a sufferer to become hospitalised.

Gluten-free grains and products made from them include amaranth, buckwheat, quinoa, millet, rice and rice milk, sorghum, sweetcorn (maize), polenta and cornflower, tapioca, teff. Other gluten-free foods include tamari soya sauce, pulses (including tofu and soya milk), nuts (including almond, hazelnut and cashew milk), mustard, many brands of chocolate (check the label, as gluten-free ones tend to advertise the fact), some yeast extracts (some contain barley extract, so check), all oils (including margarine), fruit, vegetables, seeds, wine, distilled vinegars and spirits.

Oats and gram (chickpea) flour are gluten-free if you buy them from a manufacturer who has taken care to avoid contamination when milling and certified them as gluten-free. Otherwise, always assume they contain small amounts of gluten. A small number of people with coeliac disease are also sensitive to avenin, another protein in oats.

Gluten-free brands of bread, pastry and cakes often contain eggs to bind them and add moisture, so being gluten-free and vegan is a challenge if you like to eat a lot of processed foods. However, caterers are becoming increasingly allergy aware, and as a lot of people allergic to wheat are also allergic to dairy products, the gluten-free option on a menu is quite often the vegan option.

If catering for a gluten-free friend or relative and you are unfamiliar with this type of cooking, don't panic. Curry and rice is a good staple, and normal pasta can be replaced with corn or buckwheat-based pasta from a health food shop or "free from" supermarket aisle. Or use gnocchi. When using gluten-free flour to make pastry, you'll find it can dry out and crack when cooked. To avoid this, add extra fat, water and some xanthan gum. Make sure you don't offer a coeliac guest part-used jars of jam or tubs of margarine. Open new ones, so you can guarantee that no lurking bread crumbs are in there.

Type "gluten-free vegan" into a search engine to find lots of online solidarity and recipes.

Most likely to say: "What type of soya sauce is in your stir-fry?"

Least likely to say: "Pass the garlic bread."

Guru Followers

We've come across a range of self-appointed spiritual leaders with a vegan focus, who encourage their followers to adopt a lifestyle free of animal products. For example, the Loving Hut chain of vegan Chinese cafés promote the message "Be Vegan, Make Peace", and show videos of their spiritual leader, Supreme Master Ching Hai, urging diners to live a compassionate life.

We've encountered meditation centres in mid Wales, raw food retreats in Spain and new age Christians in Cornwall.

Following a guru doesn't appeal to Alex or Ronny at all, as we prefer to get our inspiration from a range of sources, however it works for some people who prefer to be advised what to think rather than having to work it out for themselves. One analogy is buying a computer with all the software you could need already on it.

There are also gurus with a non-spiritual focus that attract followers by writing books and giving lectures, such as nutrition and raw food evangelists whose opinions get quoted as gospel. We advise a healthy dose of scepticism.

Most likely to say: "I've found myself."

Least likely to say: "Some of their claims are bullshit."

Health Enthusiasts

For some people, veganism is about keeping their bodies free of saturated fat, growth hormones, pus cells in dairy and other nasties. In fact, these people rarely refer to themselves as "vegan" nowadays, preferring the ethically neutral "plant-based". Trend-setting American doctors prescribe a low-fat wholefood vegan diet as a way to reverse heart disease, and high profile middle-aged men such as former American president Bill Clinton went plant-based for this reason.

This is a much bigger tribe in America than in Europe, and as a result, American vegan literature has a greater focus on health than ethics.

Most likely to say: "I lost twenty pounds, drink alkaline water and feel fantastic."

Least likely to say: "Pass the salt."

Macrobiotics

This is a Japanese wholefood diet that's mostly or completely vegan. Macrobiotics is based on well-chewed whole grains such as brown rice and soba (buckwheat) noodles, plus steamed vegetables, pulses, seaweed, tofu and tempeh, nuts, seeds and seasonal fruit. There's a strong emphasis on local produce and adapting dishes according to the seasons. Stimulants such as caffeine tend to be avoided.

The theory is that foods contain yin and yang qualities, and that these must be kept in balance. Some macrobiotic enthusiasts eat fish, though not meat or dairy products. The Macrobiotic Association of Great Britain website contains lots of colourful, seasonal vegan recipes.

Most likely to say: "Chew every mouthful very carefully."

Least likely to say: "I'm bored with rice."

Plant-Based People

These people are not properly vegan; they eat a plant-based diet. They make this distinction, because to them, avoiding animal products is a personal preference, for health and hygiene reasons. They don't subscribe to the all-encompassing philosophical and ethical stance of veganism, and are unlikely to regard being carelessly given small amounts of food containing animal products as a massive, upsetting violation of their rights. Plant-based eaters are unlikely to go the extra mile in avoiding animal-tested or environmentally-destructive products and may not even give these issues any thought at all.

Most likely to say: "Don't call me vegan. I'm not on the scene."

Least likely to say: "Avocados may not be ethical."

Pretenders

A relatively new tribe, they have some things in common with Plant-based People, in that they don't truly embrace the ethical philosophy of veganism. The significant, and very frustrating difference is that the Pretenders call themselves vegan, even though they aren't. We're referring to people who join vegan groups on social media, go to meetups, or even join vegan dating sites, yet they willingly consume animal products some or all of the time, with no intention of giving this up.

The Pretenders have varied motivations, which can range from wanting the kudos of calling themselves vegan, without actually making any effort, wanting to be part-time plant-based, with the option of eating meat etc. at family gatherings, being confused about what "vegan" actually means (we have come across people who claim that fish aren't animals, for example, because they don't breathe air!) or, even worse, they actively seek to deceive other people. There are more vegan women than men, especially in the over 30 age group, and we've come across men on dating sites and apps who pretend to be vegan or in the process of going vegan, so that they can attract women. Once in an established relationship, they'll drop the act.

Some Pretenders regard themselves as "flexitarian", in that they'll eat vegan food while with a particular circle of friends, so as to fit in, and then eat animal products while on their own, or with different friends. Some spend years bouncing around like this, without ever being completely vegan. This can be quite damaging, as it makes the rest of us look insincere.

Raw Fooders

This diet consists of fruits, green leafy and other vegetables, nuts, seeds, fermented vegetables, mushrooms and sprouted pulses.

Many also eat dehydrated foods, which have been dried slowly at very low temperatures, typically below 42 or 48 degrees Celsius. Fruits and vegetables contain enzymes that are destroyed during cooking, and this alternative method of processing preserves the enzymes in the food. However, there is no scientific evidence to support the claim that these enzymes survive our digestive system anyway, or bring any health benefit to us.

Furthermore, while it's true that raw foods are higher in some nutrients, cooking food may also make other nutrients more absorbable, for example the phytochemicals beta-carotene (an antioxidant that converts to vitamin A) and lycopene have been shown to be better absorbed when cooked. On the other hand, due to the high amount of whole plant foods, raw food diets are very high in fibre, minerals, vitamins and other antioxidants and phytonutrients.

The many raw food gurus, some of whom call themselves "Dr" despite not having an M.D. or relevant PhD, constantly contradict each other about what constitutes the ideal raw food diet. For example, one will say "Eat only whole, local fruit and veg," versus "Have some of this magic powder (such as maca, lucuma or baobab) from the other side of the world which I just happen to be selling for £30 a kilo." And "Eat raw chocolate, which I also happen to be selling," versus "Chocolate is poison." We don't know who's "right", but we do know that selective citation by people who are selling stuff was what got us the catastrophic original four food groups back in the 1950s.

We suspect that 90% of any raw food system is likely to be spot on and 10% will be dubious, but right now nobody can prove which 10%.

Most likely to say: "Raw is our birthright. You're all burning your food."

Least likely to say: "I could murder a toasted bagel."

Religious Practitioners

Many religions have a strong vegan theme, in fact the Bible is full of teachings from Christ that involve loving animals and rejecting all human and animal slavery. Seventh-day Adventists have a strong health focus and are big advocates of a vegan diet. Quakers are staunch pacifists and many try to live a lifestyle with no violence and killing.

Hinduism has the underlying concept of *ahimsa* (dynamic harmlessness) and Jains believe that people can be reincarnated as animals, so if you are cruel to an animal, you could be hurting your own deceased relatives. Islam teaches that animals are individuals with rights and Buddhism focuses on living a peaceful, compassionate life. Hare Krishnas staunchly promote vegetarianism, though they tend to consume a lot of dairy products. Jewish grocers sell many dairy-free products such as biscuits, chocolate and ice cream, since their religion prohibits eating milk and meat in the same meal. There are societies and websites dedicated to the promotion of vegan and vegetarian living within almost every religion.

Most likely to say: "Jesus was vegan."

Least likely to say: "No gods, no masters."

Spiritual Seekers of Truth

There are many diverse types of spiritual practice that are not part of any organised religion. New Age spirituality says things like, we are all made of source energy and thus are connected to every person, animal and plant. This source energy can be thought of as love, light, power, electricity or even God. It's the divine creative force, and our spirit bodies are formed of this force. We live our earthly experience in physical bodies, whether human or animal.

Spirituality doesn't necessarily involve following a religion; in fact many practitioners actively reject the whole concept of a religion involving an external God, priests, morality and following a book of rules that says it's OK to dominate certain animals or certain people.

The spiritual vegan tribe seeks to live as compassionately as possible, through interacting with animals, nature and other people in as loving and non-violent a way as possible. Meditation is used by many to still the mind and calm emotions, allowing loving intuition to break through our cluttered thoughts.

Beware! A few people get into spirituality as a way of seeking attention or trying to find a purpose in life and they aren't necessarily consistent in the way they express themselves. Some later drop their vegan lifestyle "for spiritual reasons" by arguing that an animal spirit "told them" that they don't mind being farmed and killed. This is not spirituality; it's just a self-deceiving rationalisation for doing whatever they want without accepting responsibility for its impact on others.

Events and festivals with a spiritual and holistic focus can attract quacks and charlatans who make easy money out of the naïve and gullible with little understanding of science. They market woo-woo products such as spirals that "energise" water with "life force" to have health-giving properties, or magnetic bracelets that they claim cure illness. Some also claim that going celibate somehow makes you more pure. Be sceptical.

Most likely to say: "I learned who I really am. I am love and light."

Least likely to say: "I hate everybody."

Skinny Bitches

In 2005 the book *Skinny Bitch* was published and went on to sell over three million copies and join the New York Times Bestseller list. Widely cited as one of the most entertaining diet and cookery books ever published, it gained a celebrity fan in Victoria Beckham (Posh Spice) and became compulsive reading for many young women.

The book was written by a former model and a modelling agent. It has a punchy, no-nonsense tone and the kind of caustic humour that previous vegan books lacked. It spawned a series of follow ups, such as *Skinny Bitch in the Kitch* (a recipe book), *Bun in the Oven* (about pregnancy), *Skinny Bastard* (a less impressive version for men) and the inspirational journal *Skinny Bitchin'* which is full of motivational quotes.

The Skinny Bitch tribe are busy, sociable, straight-talking, image-conscious women who like to look good and live an ethical way. They smash just about every stupid old stereotype about vegan hippies.

Most likely to say: "I've got a hot pair of Fairtrade jeans that show off my awesome ass."

Least likely to say: "Fashion degrades women."

Straight Edgers *by Rudy Penando*

Rudy co-foundef *Pogo*, London's first vegan cafe, and founded *VX*, the first vegan shop in London, and the first vegan Merch company in the UK, called *Secret Society of Vegans*.

> *"I don't eat roast beef or fish*
> *Porky Pig is not my dish*
> *Just go ahead and let your chickens be"*

Chicken Squawk by the punk band MDC is a silly song, but it changed my life in the late 80's. The band from Austin, Texas, was known for their political lyrics and aggressive music style. They were raging against everything a punk band from Texas would: authority, sexism, police, religion, capitalism… and surprisingly against killing animals.

They were not the first band to have a militant vegetarian lifestyle.

British punk band Crass probably started it all. After they disbanded in 1984, a wave of bands sprung up and it seemed that, to be part of the scene, not only did you have to dress in black and hate British Conservative Prime Minister Margaret Thatcher, but you also had to be vegetarian.

Probably similarly influenced by Crass and the myriad of bands keeping their spirit alive, the new breed of punk bands in the U.S. that became known as 'hardcore punk' would also include the vegetarian/vegan message in their music. It became particularly the case with the second wave of Straight Edge bands coming out of the East Coast. Straight Edge is a term coined by Ian Mackaye (Minor Threat, Fugazi) back in 1981: it means you don't use drugs, smoke or drink alcohol. A total act of rebellion against society if you ask me. Ian Mackaye, who has been vegan for more than 30 years, never really mentioned anything about animal rights in his lyrics. We had to wait for the second generation of Straight Edge kids coming out of New York in 1986-1988 (Youth Crew) for vegetarianism to become part of the very popular then Straight Edge movement. Youth Of Today in 1988 released their song "No More" which forever associated Straight Edge with vegetarianism.

> *"Meat eating flesh eating think about it*
> *So callous to this crime we commit*
> *Always stuffing our face with no sympathy*
> *What a selfish, hardened society so*
> *No More"*

Youth Of Today – 'No More'

Other bands at the time, like Cro Mags or Gorilla Biscuits, were playing good and positive music. They looked great; they had an influence on me and millions of other kids around the globe. By the mid 90s, these same kids took the vegetarian / Straight Edge message and made it even more radical. And this is how veganism became the unofficial fourth law of Straight Edge. We can thank bands like Earth Crisis for that. Their blend of metal and eco-warrior attitude brought life back to the Straight Edge scene. Being vegan became cool for millions of suburban kids all over the U.S. and Europe.

Punk, Straight Edge, Vegan Edge... so many of us started a personal revolution and awakened to the concept of animal rights because we were teenagers and a band on stage was playing the most powerful music we had ever heard and singing about not killing animals. They took something from the hippies and made it cool.

Suspicious Minds

A small but very vocal tribe who start off as health enthusiasts but then go much further. This tribe believe that most aspects of modern life, such as technology, wi-fi and vaccinations, are a threat to them and their children. They'll waffle on about the dangers of microwave ovens, doctors, electronic radiation and sugar, and they always have an array of magazine articles, websites and pseudo-scientific studies to back them up. Their way is the "true" vegan way, and they can get very upset when challenged.

Most likely to say: "Mobile phone masts cause cancer."

Least likely to say: "I drink tap water, cos bottled water is a rip-off."

Trolls

Vegan internet forums and social media groups attract people who devote much of their time to arguing with us about everything from vitamin B12 to hormones in soya beans. It's a mystery why these people devote so much of their time and energy to this and we can only guess that most of them used to have a vegan lifestyle, or their ex-partner did, who dumped them. Or they simply want to stir things up and see us as an easy target. It may be they are venting their displaced anger from other unresolved areas of their lives.

Some people who eat a plant-based diet will pick fights with others about issues like not feeding cats any meat, sustainable palm oil, or claiming that some medical experiments on animals are necessary. Some are mostly vegan but harp on about honey or fish being really healthy. Some raw fooders will go on forums to rant about all cooked food being "toxic".

We recommend just ignoring the trolls. They feed on your attention.

Most likely to say: "If you need B12 from tablets, your diet is unnatural."

Least likely to say: "I don't care what people say on the internet."

Veeks (vegan geeks)

Star Trek fans often cite the iconic, pointy-eared character Spock as one of the most famous vegetarians in the galaxy, with the series mentioning that the Vulcan people do not eat meat. There are other references throughout the films and re-boots to the Star Fleet staff eating a plant-based diet and to how their society "used to" farm animals for food.

Vegan ethics are fairly common amongst programmers, DIY technology enthusiasts, hacktivists (social or political activists who infiltrate computer systems) and open-source software users. The late Steve Jobs, who founded *Apple* computers, is held up as an example of a geek entrepreneur with vegan tendencies, and the San Francisco area is full of both vegan-friendly restaurants and I.T. start-ups.

Naturally, you'll find a lot of Veeks posting their views on the internet, and they tend to get very frustrated by fundamentalists and others who make wild claims that aren't easily backed up by scientific studies. They have the Trolls for breakfast.

Most likely to say: "My new smartphone app filters out non-vegan products from my online shop."

Least likely to say: "Mobile phone masts give you cancer."

Many people come to veganism as a result of contact with a tribe's members, books, magazines, web presence or even music. Some remain in that tribe for life, while others move around. We suggest that you explore whatever interests you and create your own personal version of veganism.

CHAPTER 5
Beyond Food

VEGAN SHOES AND CLOTHING

Why vegan shoes?

It's horrifying to realise that we are still wearing animals on our feet as shoes and around our waists as belts. Whilst few today would wear fur, it can come as a shock to realise that leather and suede are also animal skins. The outer hairs have been removed chemically, and flesh scraped off the inside by a machine. Like dairy and eggs, leather and suede are part of the meat business.

We don't eat the inside and we won't wear the outside. Vegans at some point stop buying leather.

What's the alternative?

Modern synthetic leathers such as Lorica are used to manufacture 21st century vegan shoes, clothing, vehicle and airplane seats and furniture. Lorica breathes like leather, letting perspiration out, but doesn't let water in, which is great news if you've just stepped in a deep puddle.

Where to buy

There are a few dedicated shoe shops that were set up by vegans as an alternative to high street shops, with the same personal service and opportunity to try things on. In the UK these include *Vegetarian Shoes* in Brighton, *The Third Estate* in London, and *Alternative Stores* in Plant-Based Valley, Northumberland.

What if you don't live near a vegan shoe shop? The above businesses sell online too, and there are many more online vegan catalogues offering a vast selection of shoes and boots, especially in Britain, USA, Germany and Italy. You can also buy belts, jackets, bags, wallets and T-shirts.

A fun and convenient way to buy vegan shoes, boots and accessories is at one of the hundreds of vegan festivals each year around the UK and in other countries, where there might be several stalls run by vegan shoe companies. As well as vegan festivals near you, you could treat yourself to a fantastic weekend away visiting one of the huge two-day vegan festivals in Manchester, London, Bristol, Brighton, Paris, Berlin and other European or American cities, where there can be anything from 150 to over 300 stalls of vegan delights and many rooms of free talks by experts and celebrities, workshops, cookery demos, films, musicians and children's entertainers.

You can find excellent vegan sandals made by international clothing brands in outdoor clothing and camping shops. *Crocs* make waterproof clogs in a huge range of colours, originally designed for yachting, but now popular with gardeners, chefs and waiters for their ruggedness, comfort and being slip resistant. Recently some of the biggest high street chain stores have launched their own ranges of vegan shoes, bags and accessories. Vegan clothing is an explosive trend.

Not just leather

Vegans avoid buying wool, which is the fur of sheep, because it is incorrect to think that the sheep don't mind having it removed. Shearing is a violent, painful process, in which the timid sheep are thrown on their backs and are usually left with cuts and bruises. A lot of wool comes from Australia, a hot country where many sheep die from heat exhaustion and dehydration. As with dairy cows, sheep are slaughtered for meat at a relatively young age when their wool is losing quality. Wool and mutton, once again they're all the same bloody animal slave industry.

Alternatives to wool include cotton, hemp and various other plant fibres. Synthetics such as *Gore-Tex* and *Thinsulate*, popular with mountaineers and motorcyclists, can be warmer, lighter, breathable and waterproof.

As with food, in the 21st century a vegan lifestyle is not so much about giving up things as it is about replacing them with superior, kind alternatives. It's a lot easier than you might previously have thought. If you don't want to throw them away, you can give your animal skins to a charity shop, which will avoid another person buying new ones. If you can't afford to buy replacements, wear them until they fall apart then buy something kinder next time. You'll also be spared the risk of embarrassment if cocky meat-eaters point at your clothing and accuse you of hypocrisy.

HOUSEHOLD PRODUCTS AND COSMETICS

Many people prefer to buy cleaning and body care products that have not been tested on animals. But truly cruelty-free products also contain no animal ingredients, such as lanolin from wool; gelatine made from boiled up skin, hooves and bones; or stearic acid, stearin and stearates which might be made from pig or cow fat, though can also come from plants.

The good news is that it's easy to find vegan household cleaner, laundry powder, soap, shampoo, toothpaste, makeup and even candles.

Companies have woken up to the importance of clear labelling, so a quick scan of the package will usually advise you whether a product "contains no animal products" and is certified free from animal-tested ingredients.

In the UK, the Cruelty Free International "leaping bunny" logo shows that a product and its ingredients have not been *tested* on animals, but does not tell you whether any of those ingredients were *made from* animals. To verify whether a product labelled "cruelty-free" is in fact free from all animal suffering, look for the words "free from animal ingredients", "entirely plant-based" or "vegan". The Vegan Society trademark does guarantee both no animal testing and no animal ingredients.

"Cruelty-free" without the leaping bunny certification, "Product not tested on animals", and "We explore alternatives to animal testing" are all meaningless marketing terms. The ingredients may still be tested on animals, or derived from them. Look for more solid declarations, like "No animal testing," and "Contains no animal ingredients". The Vegan Society trademark guarantees all of that.

Here are our tips for shopping in the UK:

Supermarket own brands are a really good starting point these days, as many are vegan and free from animal testing. According to a survey in 2019 by *Vegan Food & Living* magazine of 8,300 people in the UK, the Co-op, Sainsbury's and Tesco are the most consistent with their labelling of cosmetics and household products. For example, Aldi own brand cleaning products all carry the leaping bunny logo to show they are not tested on animals, but some contain animal ingredients.

Superdrug is the best high street chemist for vegan toiletries.

Lush is a chain of completely vegetarian shops selling soap, shampoo, shower gel, lip balm and other cosmetics. 80% of products are vegan and clearly labelled.

If you want the most ethical products, produced with the environment in mind, buy from wholefood shops, which stock brands such as Faith in Nature and Bio-D. Some offer a refill service to save on packaging, and this is always the case in the new trend of zero packaging wholefood stores.

Beware that some items sold in wholefood shops may contain bee products such as beeswax, honey or propolis.

Some companies are expanding into China, where animal testing is required by law on products sold in shops, so buying their products may fund animal testing, even if it's not done in Europe. Therefore, some companies refuse to sell in China. Alternatively, by selling only via a specialist online channel, cruelty-free European companies have been able to avoid the Chinese requirement for animal testing.

Although it is widely believed that cosmetics and household product testing on animals ended in the European Union in 2012, this isn't entirely true. Some ingredients are still tested, even if the final products aren't. Plus, at the time of going to print, Britain is leaving the EU, and this could have an impact.

ALCOHOLIC DRINKS

Alcoholic drinks are almost always made with entirely vegan ingredients, with the exception of Irish Cream liqueurs which contain actual cream, and Advocaat, which contains egg yolk. However, the way in which many of them are cleared of sediment (fined or cleared) can involve animal products like isinglass (from fish), egg shells, egg white, blood and gelatine. So if you're strict about your vegan lifestyle, you may want to avoid buying from breweries and wine producers that do this, and instead choose un-fined drinks, or support more modern, animal-free methods.

Spirits

Whisky and brandy are always totally vegan, as are almost all lagers and cloudy ciders. Wine and beer are the drinks most likely to be made using animal products.

Wine

It's a closely-guarded industry secret that a bottle of wine can contain all kinds of nasties. Grapes are a delicate fruit, and an arsenal of toxic chemicals is employed to blast the voracious bugs and fungi that infest them. There are over 50 pesticides in use by the wine industry, which puts vineyard workers, our environment, and you, the drinker, at risk. However, the good news is that there's an increasing demand for organic wine, and it is now very easy to find in off-licences, supermarkets and other shops.

Although gelatine is less often used as a 'fining' (clarifying) agent, to make tiny particles in the wine stick together so they can be filtered out, the fish extract isinglass is still added to many wines, regardless of whether they're organic, and it's very unlikely to be listed on the label. Many vegetarian wines are cleared with beaten egg white. The good news is that wine labelling is getting better, and milk and eggs used for fining now need to be labelled by law as they are allergens.

If you want to be sure that your wine is both free from toxic chemicals and cleared with clay rather than animal products, you can get it from a health food shop, a large supermarket, or a specific vegan wine supplier. It used to be very difficult to find vegan wines in supermarkets, though this has changed dramatically in recent years, with almost all own-brand bottles and quite a few other brands having allergy warnings and vegan status listed in small print on the back label. A quick browse is all that's needed. Also, there is a fashion for raw, unfiltered wines, which have a little sediment in the bottle, because they haven't been cleared. These are common in France and often very cheap.

Beer and cider

Beer and cider production, like wine, often involves animal products in the fining process to help remove impurities and improve the appearance of the final product. EU and UK legislation does not require breweries to list ingredients in any drinks with an alcoholic content of more than 1.2% volume - so usually you don't know by the label if it is vegetarian or vegan. Fortunately, many cask and keg beers and ciders are animal-free and use either bentonite (a type of clay) or pea extract for fining, or are left longer to settle. Unlike wines, popular beers and ciders are generally branded clearly and it is nearly always possible to find some in a pub or supermarket.

Bottle-conditioned real ales are almost always vegan because they are not filtered. Yeast needs to be in the bottle in order for it to continue fermenting. The same applies to cloudy ciders. Lagers are brewed in a different way to beer, and are usually (though not always) chill-filtered.

As a general rule, most cask-conditioned ales on tap in pubs, and even some bottled ales, are fined with isinglass (fish).

All German beers and lagers and most Dutch, Czech and Belgian ones are vegan, as are some British brands that are available in almost every supermarket, such as *Badger* and *Shepherd Neame*. We haven't included a longer list as it would go out of date soon after publication, but you can find up to date lists of vegan drinks by googling, for example, vegan wine.

The Sam Smiths pub chain sells a variety of beers from their own breweries at affordable prices, and 90% are certified with the Vegan Society, though there's no guarantee of vegan food on the menu. The Brewdog chain of pubs clearly label their vegan beers, and all of them have some vegan items on the fast food menu.

Online Vegan Booze Directory

barnivore.com

veganwomble.com, Categories, Vegan Drinks

Vegan alcohol mail order

Vinceremos.co.uk

Vintageroots.co.uk

VEGAN PET FOOD

by vegan vet Prof Andrew Knight

A thought-provoking examination of the controversial issue of vegan diets for cats and dogs. Includes a discussion of the health hazards and benefits of meat-based and vegan diets, a discussion of natural feeding behaviour, and advice for guardians of vegan animals on safeguarding their health.

Meat based pet food

Despite the biological evidence, millions of people cling to the belief that it is somehow natural to feed their feline or canine companions commercial diets comprised of assorted body parts from a variety of animals they would never naturally eat. To these are added abattoir products condemned as unfit for human consumption, such as '4-D' meat (from animals that are disabled, diseased, dying or dead on arrival at the abattoir), cleverly disguised using names like 'meat derivatives' or 'by-products.'

Brands from countries such as the US also contain rendered dog and cat carcasses sourced from animal shelters. Similarly, toxic flea collars are not always removed. Unsurprisingly, a 1998 US Food and

Drug Administration study detected the euthanizing solution sodium pentobarbital, which is specifically designed to kill dogs, cats and other animals, in 43 randomly-selected varieties of dry dog food.

To enhance palatability, dry food is sprayed with a combination of refined animal fat, lard, used restaurant grease and other oils considered too rancid or inedible for human consumption, containing high levels of unhealthy free radicals and trans fatty acids. These oils provide the distinctive smell that wafts from a newly-opened packet of kibble.

Additional hazards include bacterial, protozoal, fungal, viral and prion contaminants, along with their assorted endotoxins and mycotoxins; hormone and antibiotic residues, particularly in brands from countries such as the US, where more of these chemicals are administered to livestock; and potentially dangerous preservatives, some of which have been banned in various countries.

Vegan diets: a healthy alternative

Properly formulated vegan diets can provide a healthy alternative for both cats and dogs, eliminating the numerous hazards inherent to meat-based pet food. They supply all required nutrients using only vegetable, mineral and synthetic sources. Each species requires particular dietary nutrients, after all, rather than specific ingredients.

A growing number of manufacturers now supply vegan companion animal diets, both complete diets and dietary supplements. The former offer convenience, while the latter provide a cheaper alternative for those wishing to add nutritional supplements to home-made diets. Recipes are available in books such as *Vegetarian Cats & Dogs* (Peden, 1999) and *Obligate Carnivore* (Gillen, 2003), and from suppliers.

But is it healthy?

In 2006 the first study of the health of a population of long-term vegetarian cats (most, in fact, were vegan), was published in the Journal of the American Veterinary Medical Association, one of the world's leading veterinary journals. Most were clinically healthy, barring minor deficiencies in three cats who were fed partly on table scraps. Similarly, a 1994 study of a population of vegan and vegetarian dogs found the vast majority to be in good to excellent health, particularly in lifetime vegans or vegetarians. Based on numerous additional reported cases, nutritionally-sound vegan or vegetarian companion animal

Vegan Dog & Cat Food

plant based complete foods and treats

Since 2003, VeggiePets.com has been supplying ethical, healthy, alternative pet products all over the UK and the world! Providing a wide selection of Vegetarian and Vegan dog and cat foods and natural dog chews & biscuits.
As well as biodegradable cat litters, compostable poop bags, supplements, and cruelty free grooming products.

...and more!

Shop online at www.VeggiePets.com

Tel: 023 9245 3355 or write to VeggiePets.com, c/o Vegeco Ltd, Unit 4, Downley Business Park, 12 Downley Rd, Havant, PO9 2NJ

diets may be associated with the following health benefits: increased overall health and vitality, decreased incidences of cancer, infections, hypothyroidism (an important hormonal disease), ectoparasites (fleas, ticks, lice and mites), improved coat condition, allergy control, weight control, arthritis regression, diabetes regression and cataract resolution.

Health issues

Correct use of a complete and balanced nutritional supplement or complete diet is essential to prevent the nutritional diseases that will otherwise eventually occur, if certain dietary nutrients are deficient.

Changing to a vegan diet may result in urinary alkalinisation, which can increase the risk of urinary stones and blockages, especially in male cats. These can be life-threatening. Hence, regular monitoring of the urine acidity of both sexes of cats and dogs is essential, weekly during any dietary transition, and monthly after stabilisation. Urine can be collected from dogs using containers such as foil baking trays, and from cats using non-absorbent plastic cat litter available from veterinarians. pH (acidity) test strips are also available from veterinarians, although pH meters provide the most accurate results. The pH of cat and dog urine is normally 6.0 – 7.5, where 7.0 is neutral, and lower numbers indicate acidity. A variety of dietary additives listed at VegePets.info can correct alkalinisation, should it occur.

Illustrations © Copyright Marc Vyvyan-Jones

Conclusions

Perhaps one day you'll be the first to spot a house-cat chasing tuna whilst floating along on that tropical island holiday your boss surely owes you. Perhaps you'll be the first to acquire hard evidence that it's natural for cats and dogs to eat fish, or any of the other incongruous and potentially hazardous ingredients in meat-based pet foods. Until then, however, you might want to consider a nutritionally-sound vegan alternative. This would maximise the chances of good health and longevity for not only your cat or dog, but also, of course, our frequently mistreated, so-called 'food' animals! Tips on transitioning to vegan diets and a comprehensive list of brands and suppliers are available at VegePets.info.

Excerpted with updates from Knight A. *Fishy business?*
in *Lifescape* magazine, 2008 (May) 74-76.

Prof Andrew Knight is a European Veterinary Specialist in Welfare Science, Ethics & Law. He is Professor of Animal Welfare and Ethics, and Founding Director of Winchester University's Centre for Animal Welfare. He authors the informational site VegePets.info

CHAPTER 6
Family and Friends

BEING VEGAN IN A PRE-VEGAN WORLD

Almost every social event involves food, so there will be situations where your diet becomes the topic of conversation, curiosity, or confusion.

We can be surprised at the strength of the resistance to, or criticism of, our veganism from family, friends, and school or college or work colleagues. This chapter tells you how to help the people in your life understand and adapt to your way of eating by explaining your choices in a non-confrontational way.

Attempting to instantly convert everyone you meet by bombarding them with information about veganism could annoy them and actually put them off. So as well as knowing the facts about veganism, you also need to know about effective communication techniques, and choose what to say, how to say it, and just as importantly how not to say it, in each situation.

You may prefer not to discuss your diet unless it's necessary, or you may relish the opportunity to explain and even promote veganism with everyone. Neither is right or wrong; each vegan has to find his or her own way of living in a meat-eating world.

Becoming vegan can make some people uncomfortable, but this discomfort may not be all bad. It could eventually get them thinking more carefully about their own food choices.

If you are a young person who is still living with your parents, and trying to turn vegan, the next two pages may be helpful.

Level 1 Vegan – state your food needs, without justifying

Politely and clearly state what you want to eat to your family,
and before or at social events.

We believe it is your human right to decide what does or does not
go into your body, and you do not even need to give a reason beyond
"I don't eat that" or "I do eat these." Just like someone with a peanut
allergy or religious objection to particular foods.

Level 2 Vegan – answer questions

Provide information when people ask questions such as where
do you get your protein from, or why are you vegan. All those
answers are in this book.

Level 3 Vegan – defend against attacks

Some people believe meat and dairy are essential. There is a lot of
wrong information out there, and it can be very convincing to
people who already eat and enjoy such foods. With the best of
intentions, they may try to convince you to eat like them.

What can you do to respond to your family's resistance to veganism
and attempts to influence you to revert to being non-vegan?
There are a number of strategies:

Become informed

Learn as much as you can about the arguments for veganism in terms
of animal suffering, health, environmental destruction, land and water
use, economics and social justice. You will be more credible if your
passion is supported by facts.

Discussions provide information, whereas quarrels leave
everyone feeling bad.

Identify any specific issues that interest your family and focus on them.
For example, if someone is interested in health, focus on those benefits
of a vegan diet rather than trying to discuss social justice or animal
cruelty. Those conversations can come later.

Manage strong emotion

Bring yourself to a state of calm so you can have productive
conversations about these very challenging subjects, without becoming
afraid, angry or sad.

Learn to slow your breathing; use self-soothing self-talk techniques; develop a positive mindset and reframe. Cognitive reframing is a psychological technique that consists of identifying and then changing the way situations, experiences, events, ideas, and emotions are viewed, by challenging and then changing them. It is a general change in one's mindset.

Don't rush

Move other people towards understanding your veganism in steps, during a series of conversations.

Do not demand that they become vegan. That only creates what psychologists call *reactance*. Reactance occurs when a person feels that someone is taking away their choices, an unpleasant motivational arousal to rules that threaten specific behavioural freedoms. In this case, their right to eat whatever they want. Provide information and leave them to think about why you are vegan. Let them know that you will be available if they want to discuss it further.

It is extremely unusual for people to become vegan after just one conversation, though it sometimes happens if they are already vegetarian. Your goal is not to turn them vegan, but to get them to understand why you have chosen to be vegan. Becoming vegan or not is their decision. Your job is to make veganism look good, easy and fun. Sharing food can be a great start.

Get support

Surround yourself with other vegans who understand you, and gain their help and support. This could be in online discussion groups, or at your local vegan social or campaigning group. Regularly share with them your experiences, and work with them to become the best advertisement for veganism that you can be.

If someone is attempting to pressure or bully you into eating animal products, contact a vegan organisation for support. Veganism is an ethical belief, protected in some countries just like a religion, and a national organisation can help you stand your ground and reassure your parents that your choices are at least as healthy as theirs. Up to date information written by doctors and dietitians is really helpful here. When your parents understand that your choice will not cause deficiencies, and that you are caring and compassionate, their fear and anger can dissolve and be replaced by pride.

For a list of vegan organisations, see chapter 8.

Level 4 Vegan - teacher

When you're good at being vegan and explaining it, you might choose to get active and become a vegan evangelist, or vegangelist.

Many people can be reached by providing information about animal suffering.

Some people, especially those in the second half of life, respond well to information about health.

Some respond well to information about the environment and global heating. We need to plant a lot of trees to absorb carbon. In order to do this, we have to release land by stopping animal farming.

People who go vegan, or at least cut down on animal products, for their health or for the planet, may later get interested in the animal cruelty arguments too. A handful of (usually fairly angry) vegans will tell you you're not a "proper" vegan unless you do it "for the animals." We disagree, even though we ourselves are animal rights vegans. The animals and the planet don't care why people initially go vegan, all that matters is that one way or another the cruelty and destruction end. Whichever door someone came through to discover veganism, whether for health, animals, or the planet, eventually most vegans see the importance and interdependence of all three.

Videos on Youtube and documentary films on Netflix, such as *Forks Over Knives* or *What the Health*, are really useful. It's one thing to read, but quite another to actually see the reality. Not just what is evil about the current agriculture and food industries, but also what is wonderful about the vegan alternatives.

Easiest of all, and lots of fun, is simply sharing fabulous vegan food. Then it's not so much about what we are against, but what we are for, and that can be really enticing.

Be a healthy, happy vegan, a living example of the way of the vegan in action.

Level 5 Vegan – instructor trainer

Some people, like us, decide to become a professional vegan. We began by volunteering at national organisations, working alongside full-time activists, using skills we already had and learning new ones.

You might then decide to study catering, nutrition, business, marketing, psychology, journalism, law, graphic design, web design, computer science, medicine or veterinary medicine, any of which can be used within animal rights, health, environmental or food education and campaigning.

We suggest you start by learning to make irresistible vegan food. You might as well ensure you and your nearest and dearest enjoy being vegan! Activism is much more attractive if you put food on the table, whether a street stall, talk indoors, or radio or TV interview.

Learn to communicate effectively about veganism. Online talks and books by activist trainers Melanie Joy and Tobias Leenaert tell you all about this. Or you can go to activist training workshops run by national and international vegan organisations.

Ethical veganism is a protected belief

An ethical vegan is someone who opposes the use of animals by humans for any purpose. In January 2020 in a landmark legal case brought by our vegan friend Jordi Casamitjana, an employment tribunal in England ruled that ethical veganism amounts to a philosophical belief, protected against discrimination under the Equality Act 2010.

According to opinions expressed on law firm websites, this has implications for the workplace, education, transport and the provision of goods and services such as, for example, having to ensure vegan meal options, or that uniforms or office equipment be vegan-compliant.

The Equality Act provides a five-point test to determine when a philosophical belief is protected. The belief:

- Must be genuinely held. In other words, a person can't claim to have suddenly become vegan, when it is convenient to do so, and then drop this claim once they've got their own way.

- Must be a belief and not an opinion or viewpoint based on the present state of information available.

- Must be a belief as to a weighty and substantial aspect of human life and behaviour. A court would look at how the person conducts themselves in all aspects of life, to check for contradictions. A person claiming discrimination needs to prove that being vegan is central to how they live and the choices they make.

- Must attain a certain level of cogency, seriousness, cohesion and importance. If we were forced to do non-vegan things, it would cause us great distress. It's not just a preference.

- Must be worthy of respect in a democratic society, and compatible with human dignity and the fundamental rights of others.

This aligns with article 9 of the European Convention of Human Rights on the right to freedom of thought, conscience and religion, and the right to change belief, either alone or in community with others and in public or private. Freedom to manifest one's religion or beliefs is subject only to such limitations as are prescribed by law and are necessary in a democratic society in the interests of public safety, for the protection of public order, health or morals, or for the protection of the rights and freedoms of others.

A 2017 law in Portugal made it illegal not to offer vegan food at prisons, hospitals and schools.

The story of Jordi Casamitjana's life, as a campaigning vegan zoologist and research scientist specialising in animal behaviour, is told in his new book *Ethical Vegan: A Personal and Political Journey to Change the World*. Jordi has worked as an undercover investigator, animal welfare consultant and animal protection campaigner, including being involved in successful prosecutions for illegal hunting, and the campaign that led to the ban on bullfighting in Catalonia. His life is a fine example of an ethical vegan making a career out of helping to create a better world.

Resources

Facebook is full of local, national and global vegan groups, which could be based in your town or country. *Campaigning* groups organise vegan and animal rights outreach street stalls. *Social* groups arrange restaurant meals, picnics and events. *Discussion* groups are excellent for posting questions about what or where to eat and shop in your town or country or dealing with non-vegans.

The Wikipedia article on *Defence mechanism* lists ways that people unconsciously deny and distort reality. Other interesting articles are

Reactance (psychology), Cognitive dissonance, Psychology of eating meat, Carnism, Speciesism, and *Ethics of eating meat.*

Beyond Beliefs: A Guide to Improving Relationships and Communication for Vegans is a book and ebook by social psychologist Melanie Joy PhD, in which she discusses effective and ineffective communication between vegans and non-vegans. Also her website *Beyond Carnism* and Youtube videos.

How To Create A Vegan World: A Pragmatic Approach is a book and ebook by activist trainer Tobias Leenaert, who works with Melanie Joy. He examines ways of promoting veganism that actually work, and those that don't, and how we can use them to create a vegan world in the shortest time.

Animal Rights – a universal declaration is a 22-minute broadcast quality dvd scripted and co-directed by Alex Bourke, from an idea by Ronny Worsey, covering the main areas of animal rights campaigning and why we don't eat them. There are interviews with activists and the psychologist who invented the word *speciesism*, accompanied by undercover footage from farms, labs, circuses and zoos, and showing vegan food and clothing. The film can open a meeting or school talk, for example, a year 10 Citizenship class where pupils prepare to debate a topic such as should factory farming be banned. In America it has been shown by PETA in campus cinemas and broadcast on cable TV. You can watch a trailer and buy at vegetarianguides.co.uk/video. Teacher's notes and lesson plans are available.

VEGAN PARENTING

by Chrissy Leyland, vegan mother, counsellor and chef

The decision to bring up our child vegan was an easy one to make, requiring no discussion with my partner. We both took it for granted that this is what we would do as a logical extension of our belief in veganism for animals, the planet and human health.

The most challenging part of being vegan is belonging to a non-vegan world and this seems even more so when you have kids. People may accept your choice to be a vegan, but they may feel it is wrong for you to bring up a child as a vegan. These objections fit broadly into two categories:

Health: your child won't get the nutrients they need;

Social: they will feel deprived of treats and stigmatised for their diet.

While these concerns may at times annoy you, you may have concerns or questions yourself which fit into these two categories. This chapter addresses some of these concerns from my experience as a vegan parent and from listening to others. Though there may be some challenges to overcome, being a vegan parent is easier than most people imagine. We are still a minority within a minority (most parents aren't vegans and most vegans aren't parents) but there are growing numbers of parents choosing to bring their children up in this healthy, compassionate and sustainable way.

Nutrition

A plant-based diet can provide all the nutrients needed during pregnancy, breastfeeding, and for a growing child. According to the American Academy of Nutrition and Dietetics "appropriately planned vegetarian, including vegan, diets are healthful, nutritionally adequate, and may provide health benefits for the prevention and treatment of certain diseases. These diets are appropriate for all stages of the life cycle, including pregnancy, lactation, infancy, childhood, adolescence, older adulthood, and for athletes."

Just as there are many health benefits for a woman following a vegan diet at all stages of life, so too a vegan diet during pregnancy reduces the risk of food borne illnesses, and avoids foods high in saturated fat and cholesterol such as cows' milk, eggs and cheese, and reduces the risk of high blood pressure and pre-eclampsia.

Similarly, there are health benefits for our children in following a plant-based diet. In her excellent book *Feeding Your Vegan Infant – with confidence*, dietitian Sandra Hood explains that various studies have shown that, like adults, omnivore children have been falling prey to the pitfalls of the Western diet including obesity and type 2 diabetes. There is also concern about levels of dental caries and anaemia amongst children. According to Sandra "The vegan diet has the answer!" Vegan children eat more fruit and vegetables, less saturated fat and cholesterol, are lighter in weight, and have fewer dental caries than their peers.

It is even more important to become aware of nutrition during pregnancy, firstly to allay any fears from health professionals and family members, and more importantly to ensure you and your children are following a properly balanced vegan diet, so Sandra Hood's book is recommended reading. Vegan food can be higher in fibre and lower in calories than non-vegan food, and especially in the early years kids need to consume a higher calorie diet so including higher fat vegan foods is essential as is ensuring protein, calcium and iron, essential fatty acids and of course an adequate supply of B12.

Being around non-vegans

Most of the parents you meet with will probably be omnivores, so non-vegan food will be all around you!

Start explaining to your child from a young age what a vegan is and why you are vegan, which can help your child to understand why we choose not to eat the same food as other people. Even very small children can understand that it is wrong to eat animals, or to take their milk and eggs, but they will probably find it more difficult to understand why most people do nevertheless continue to eat animals. Obviously you don't want to upset a very young child with too much graphic detail of animal abuse, so you need to judge what to tell your child and at what age. Our vegan kids are exposed to the truth, and this may be difficult for them to deal with. However, they can feel good that they are not part of the suffering and don't have to deal with the conflicting emotions many non-vegan children feel about loving animals and yet eating them.

Social situations and parties

I was shocked when I first had my child how many sweets and unhealthy snacks were offered to kids at play groups and people's houses. When your kids are young it is a good idea to always carry some snacks around with you so they don't feel left out when others are given "treats." This is especially important when your kids are too young to understand being vegan.

As your child gets older they may be invited to tea on their own at friends' houses. Politely explain to the host that you are vegan and offer suggestions as to what they might provide. If necessary you can supply some of the food, e.g. pudding such as a soya dessert.

When entertaining other children, make food which they will be familiar with such as burgers, sausage and chips/beans, pizza or pasta. Vegan cakes usually go down well with children!

Parties have posed little problem for us. Speak to the host and explain you are vegan. Sometimes hosts are happy to provide vegan food, usually with some guidance, other times they prefer you to provide the food, or a combination, e.g. they will provide vegan sandwiches but you will provide sweets and a cake. Find out what sort of food is being provided so yours can be similar, and ensure everything is covered like prizes, goody bags etc. You can freeze batches of cupcakes and defrost them for parties. Bringing food for everyone to share can help your child feel more normal and do a bit of vegan promotion!

If the party is being held at a Soft Play or another commercial venue, contact the venue in advance. I have found they are normally happy to cater for you if you give some simple suggestions, and again sometimes I have provided some of the food, such as chocolates and vegan cheese for pizzas. Soft Plays have also been happy to provide a fully vegan party on Zak's birthday, which the kids have happily eaten being blissfully unaware that they are eating an animal-free meal!

Education

Unless you home educate, your vegan child will be entering into the non-vegan world of the education system. Vegan children are fine at school, but it is parents' responsibility to ensure that this goes as smoothly as possible for your child.

Catering at nursery is usually better as often parents are paying for it, and they are dealing with smaller numbers of children. Request a meeting with the kitchen staff prior to your child starting nursery and discuss a menu.

It can be harder, though not impossible, to obtain vegan school dinners. While schools are generally much better than they used to be, they vary in how good they are. The Vegan Society provides support and advice for people who wish to get school dinners for their children.

If you cannot get satisfactory school meals, you may prefer to provide packed lunches. The book and ebook *The Vegan Lunch Box* by Jennifer McCann has lots of great ideas, though Zak prefers just to have tahini and yeast extract sandwiches every day! Be aware many schools have a no nuts policy due to children with allergies, which reduces our lunch box options.

Whenever starting a new school or class it is important to explain to the teacher that your child is vegan and what this means. The Vegan Society produces a useful handout for schools with information about what being vegan means, which you can add your child's name and photo to.

You can leave a box of treats in the classroom which your child can be offered when the other children are being given some non-vegan food, e.g. sometimes kids bring sweets to share on their birthday. Choose treats that look similar and of course what your child likes best. Luckily there are now many more vegan products available that look and taste great. If kids have milk in primary school then you can provide small cartons of fortified non-dairy milk as an alternative.

Keep an eye out for activities which involve food. My experience is that teachers are generally helpful and respectful, but are busy and not used to dealing with vegans, so may forget about some situations. Every time there is an activity involving food, such as cookery lessons, discuss this with the teacher and ensure your child is catered for.

What if your partner isn't vegan?

There's no doubt that it is easier to raise your kids vegan if both parents are vegan, but it is still possible when only one parent is vegan. This is something both parents need to discuss and agree on and it depends how supportive the non-vegan parent is. It will make it easier if you can agree on only eating vegan food at home.

Can you turn non-vegan kids vegan?

It is easier for children if they have never known being non-vegan, but it is perfectly possibly for kids to make the transition to veganism. Depending on the age of the children, discuss the choice with them and find out their opinion. It is much easier to be vegan at home, so a good way to start is by eating vegan meals at home. Try giving them vegan versions of their favourite meals. How enthusiastic your kids are will determine how quickly you can transition into a vegan household.

Hostility from others

As with being vegan in general, most people will accept your choice, perhaps be curious and have questions to ask. However, some people may be hostile to your choice of diet for your child. You may be challenged by family, friends, other parents or professionals such as teachers, health visitors or your family doctor.

Being armed with the facts will help in these situations. Though it can be very distressing to have your choice questioned, often they are voicing genuine concern for the welfare of your child, having heard or read so much propaganda that animal products are essential for health. Try to stay calm and remember that what may seem obvious to you is a new idea to other people.

Their concerns will fall into two main categories: nutrition and social. Apart from the very persistently anti-vegan people, the hostility you experience will recede over time as people see that your child is happy and healthy. Once kids start to get older, they can be very good at putting the case for veganism in their own words.

Sometimes you may feel that you do not trust a relative or professional to look after your child if they may give them non-vegan food to eat. Make sure you make your position on this clear, provide adequate information and food if necessary. If your child is given something non-vegan to eat, do not get too distressed, remember the definition of veganism includes "as far as is possible and practicable." You cannot be there to watch your child 24/7 and you are doing your very best to raise them vegan.

Common questions and answers

Below are some common questions you may be asked and some suggested responses. These are just to give you some ideas. Your answer will vary depending on the age or personality of your child and our own opinions.

"Your child needs milk/meat to grow, and will get anaemic etc…"

"Vegan diets are proven to provide all the nutrients children need. There are health advantages to following a vegan diet compared to the standard western diet, e.g. veganism is higher in fruit and vegetables, lower in saturated fat, and there is less risk of food poisoning. Children do not need cows' milk to grow. Dairy products are not consumed in many traditional diets that are healthier than the western diet. Cows' milk is designed for calves not human children. Anaemia in children is often caused by drinking too much cows' milk (which contains negligible iron), and anaemia is no more common amongst vegans than meat eaters."

If they won't take your word for it, provide them with copies of useful information or direct them to the Vegan Society, which has an in-house dietitian. This may be particularly important if dealing with health professionals.

"You are imposing your beliefs on your children"

"All parents impose their beliefs on their children, it is impossible to do otherwise. If you bring your child up as an omnivore you are imposing onto your child your belief that it is acceptable to use animals for food. Just because our belief is currently a minority one it does not mean we are not entitled to bring our children up in a way we feel is ethical and healthy. Vegans have a much lower carbon footprint than meat eaters, so by bringing my child up vegan I am helping to protect the planet for all children."

"Your child will miss out on treats"

"Eating lots of sweets is not good for children. However, there now many vegan chocolates, sweets and cakes available which taste just as good as the non-vegan alternatives and are often healthier."

"Your child will feel left out or be bullied because they are vegan"

"I make every effort to ensure that my child is included. He chooses to be vegan because he understands the reasons for making this choice. The vegan community is thriving and vibrant and he feels proud to be a part of this. Bullying and excluding children is wrong and we should all challenge those who are doing this, whether intentionally or not, rather than our children having to change who they are."

"Your child will rebel and eat bacon butties when they are older!"

"Nobody knows what my child will choose to eat when he is older, and this will be his choice to make. However, many children who are brought up vegan choose to stay vegan and sometimes bring up vegan children themselves."

What if my child no longer wants to be vegan?

We cannot force our children to be vegan, we have to accept that they are individuals with their own choices to make in life. Many people who have been brought up vegan will at some point at least try animal products. I believe that anyone who eats animal products should be exposed to the truth. This is difficult though when we are dealing with children, because we are unsure how much to expose them to.

I know some vegan parents who have had children wanting to eat meat and have asked them to watch some footage of slaughter and the meat industry. If you are thinking of doing this with your child, you can make a judgement of what you think they can handle, or you can use guidelines, for example Animal Aid and Viva! have films which are suitable for children of different ages.

Talking to your child is vital and finding out why they no longer want to be vegan. Sometimes the problem can be addressed. There are no easy answers here and it has to be a dialogue between you and your child. With my child I found out the issue was that kids in his class were offered chocolates from a share bag and he felt left out. The alternative he was offered was not what he wanted and he got upset. We let him choose to have the non-vegan chocolates but he only tried a couple before deciding to be vegan again, and this time we made sure his favourite Moo Free chocolates were available!

Be gentle with your children if they are wavering about being vegan kids in a non-vegan world, it can be tough and our non-judgmental support is the best way to guide them through it. Most of the time, though, vegan kids will embrace and enjoy their diet and be proud to be vegan.

Meet other vegan parents

With many of the issues described above it can help to speak to other vegan parents for support, ideas, and for our kids so they don't feel like they are the only ones. There are several online groups where you can connect with other parents, possibly meet up, but at least talk online.

Vegan festivals, which are now happening all over the UK and other countries, usually have kids' activities and are a great way to meet other families and give your child a sense of the vegan community and how fantastic it is to be part of it!

Chrissy Leyland was a founder of Pogo Vegan Café, London Vegan Campaigns and the London Vegan Pledge, and The Vegan Approach outreach campaign in Sheffield. She holds a postgraduate diploma in Integrative Counselling.

Resources

Feeding Your Vegan Infant – with confidence: a practical guide from pre-conception through to pre-school by Sandra Hood, 2005 Out of print, available secondhand on amazon. New edition spring 2021 titled **Feeding Your Vegan Child – a practical guide to plant-based nutrition**

Veducated!: An Educator's Guide for Vegan-Inclusive Teaching, by Laura Chepner, August 2020. New British book and ebook by a vegan primary school teacher and education consultant, aimed at education professionals, to help ensure that vegan children of all ages are treated equally and inclusively. Full of facts, debunking the many myths about veganism, and ready-to-use lesson plans with the vegan child's viewpoint in mind. A perfect present for your child's class teacher.

The website vieducation.co.uk campaigns for *Vegan Inclusive Education* in UK schools.

American books available from Amazon:

Your Complete Vegan Pregnancy by Reed Mangels R.D., 2019.

Nourish: The Definitive Plant-Based Nutrition Guide for Familes by Brenda Davis R.D., December 2020.

Useful websites

Raisevegan.com is the world's largest vegan parenting community, with a monthly print magazine or app and private groups around the world.

The website plantbasedhealthprofessionals.com has a *Pediatric Plant-based Nutrition Quick Start Guide* and various fact sheets on pregnancy and feeding your baby.

These national vegan organisations specialise in helping young people, parents and teachers.
VeganSociety.com
AnimalAid.org.uk
Viva.org.uk

CHAPTER 7

Can Going Vegan Save Your Life?

*"The vast majority of premature deaths can be
prevented through simple changes in diet and lifestyle."*

Michael Greger M.D., nutritionfacts.org

Most doctors are so busy fixing people with non-infectious diseases using drugs and surgery that there's no time to deal with what's making most of them sick in the first place.

Veganism saves animals and saves the planet. A healthy vegan diet can also help you avoid the big three killers: heart disease, diabetes, and even some kinds of cancer. This has been demonstrated by pioneering vegan doctors and thousands of their patients.

HEALTH BENEFITS OF A VEGAN DIET

By vegan GP Dr Mike Hooper, MSc (Nutrition)

The undeniable truth

There's no denying that vegans are healthy. Multiple scientific studies have shown that vegetarians have lower mortality rates than people who eat meat; now veganism appears to be showing similar benefits. For example, the AHS-2 study of over 96,000 American and Canadian Seventh-day Adventists (a Christian denomination, many of whom are vegetarian or vegan) at Loma Linda University School of Public Health in California suggests that vegans may be in one of the lowest mortality diet groups, and have a lower risk of chronic disease than their contemporaries.

There's very good evidence, from this and many other studies, that vegans have, on average, lower rates of obesity, lower cholesterol and blood pressure. They also suffer from less heart disease and diabetes, and these conditions may be reversible with the right vegan diet.

Further research suggests vegans also have reduced rates of some cancers, chronic kidney disease and dementia. Some of the best dietary health studies are those on sporting people – especially runners. In these, vegans are often at the front of the pack! So there are plenty of reasons to go vegan for the sake of your own life – as well as the lives of animals and the planet.

Take the Vegan Pledge

The majority of people who took the 30-day *Vegan Pledge* with London Vegan Campaigns between 2007 and 2013 reported better health. This included reduction in levels of overweight, more energy, better skin, fewer colds and better mental health – feeling calmer and less moody. This wasn't a scientific study (for example, vegans often have healthier life habits in other respects, e.g. less smoking, more exercise) – but it's a good hint that the change may be worthwhile on a personal level. Since 2013, the Pledge principle has continued through the Vegan Society (12,000 people per year) and Veganuary (over 400,000 people worldwide in 2020) – so something must be going right.

The hazards of not being vegan

The flipside of vegans living longer in diet studies is... somebody else must not be living as long. There is an increasing weight of evidence that people who eat meat, certainly any more than once a month and possibly at all, suffer health consequences. In the AHS-2 study above, they were the only group with significantly higher death rates; other studies have shown increasing rates of heart disease and related deaths with increasing meat intake, and still others have clarified links between eating meat and diabetes, another major cause of early death.

Outside of chronic illness, we also have to consider the higher prevalence of food poisoning from animal products (despite the antibiotics routinely used in their creation); the role of intensive animal farming in the emergence and spread of new infections such as swine 'flu and bird 'flu; and even the responsibility of human impingement on the natural world (livestock and dairy farming being two of the prime motivators) for the Coronavirus pandemic of 2020, and the health impacts of global warming. It's clear that consuming animal products isn't good for any of us – even the ones who don't.

A diet for all ages

Because becoming vegan involves a choice to eat selectively, some people, including some doctors, are concerned that it may increase the risk of nutrient deficiencies. This is understandable – but serious deficiencies in vegans have not been widely reported, although care is recommended in some areas (see below). A typical "Western diet" is characterised by too much of the wrong foods, and can still give rise to deficiency; the key to any healthy diet is getting the right balance. The major dietetic associations of the UK, US and Canada agree that a balanced vegan diet is healthy and suitable for every stage of life, including pregnancy, childhood and older age.

Nutrient check

Here's a brief rundown of nutrients which are taken in at naturally lower levels on a vegan diet, and how to spot whether you might need more of them.

Protein: Although protein levels are lower in a vegan diet, this is probably a good thing. As long as you are eating a variety of foods (see the Vegan Society's *Vegan Eatwell Guide* online, and chapter 2 of this book) at your recommended level of calorie intake, you'll be getting plenty of protein; bodybuilders might need more, whatever their dietary choice.

Iron: There's debate as to whether or not vegans are truly more likely to be iron deficient, as one of the main measures of iron status also increases in inflammatory diseases, which may be more common in non-vegans. However, if you're feeling tired (perhaps even short of breath), and/or looking pale, or have fragile nails or thinning hair, you should check your iron levels with a blood test.

Calcium/Vitamin D: Bone health is a "team effort": you should try not to take excess protein or salt, have plenty of Vitamin C and K in your diet, be physically active, drink little or no alcohol and avoid smoking; however, calcium and Vitamin D are the key nutrients. Vegans who don't consume enough calcium are at greater risk of osteoporosis, which is not felt until bones become brittle and break easily in later life, but can be detected by a bone density scan before this happens. Infants who do not take enough calcium or Vitamin D are at risk of rickets (soft, weak bones and growth restriction). Vitamin D is mainly produced by your skin from sunshine in spring and summer; all UK residents are advised to consider supplementing during autumn and winter, and some groups (including breastfed babies, children aged 1-4, and people with dark skin, or who cover most of their skin when outdoors, or spend most of their time indoors) should supplement all year.

Iodine: Iodine is mainly present in milk and dairy products through supplementation of livestock and the use of iodine as a steriliser for milking machines; vegans have to look for more natural sources (see chapter 2). In adults, low (or very high) iodine intakes can cause hypothyroidism (underactive thyroid). This may show as low energy levels, weight gain, anaemia, long/heavy periods, goitre (enlarged thyroid – swelling at the front of the neck), dry/scaly skin, tingling and numbness in extremities, low mood, or forgetfulness. Thyroid function can be checked with a blood test.

If you decide to take a thyroid supplement, research this carefully, as too much iodine can cause hyperthyroidism (overactive thyroid), which can present with palpitations, goitre, heat intolerance/sweating, trembling, nervousness or agitation and is also detectable with blood testing.

Vitamin B12: All vegans should either fortify or supplement their food with B12. There is negligible B12 in a natural plant-based diet and this is the *only* vitamin you cannot obtain in meaningful amounts from one. (Farm animals are also often supplemented with cobalt, the "heart" of B12 – so it's not just the vegans who are supplementing!). Symptoms of B12 deficiency include tiredness/anaemia, itchy skin, pins and needles or numbness, poor concentration and low mood. Shooting pains in the arms or legs can be a sign of serious deficiency, and must not be ignored. B12 levels can be checked with a blood test.

Essential fatty acids (EFAs, Omega-3 fatty acids): This is new territory from a research point of view. Currently, the science tells us that all humans, especially pregnant women, babies and young children, need both short and long versions of some specialised fats in their diet. Plant-based diets tend to have less of the long ones; so vegans make the short ones longer in their bodies. Non-vegans get most of their long EFAs from oily fish; vegans must either convert or supplement. (Vegan EFA supplements are usually derived from algae, which is what the fish are eating!)

True EFA deficiency is rare, and usually found only in people whose gut absorption is compromised; however, it's possible that some vegans with low conversion rates could have EFA levels which are less than optimal. This is unlikely to show itself, but would most probably do so as dry, scaly skin or follicular keratosis (hair follicles "plugged" with hardened dead skin), although these are most commonly due to other causes. True deficiency (in hospital and research settings) has been linked to poor wound healing, more frequent infections, impaired nerve, visual and mental function, and infant/child growth restriction. Testing for suboptimal EFA balance is currently a specialist area.

Honourable mentions

The list above is pretty comprehensive; but if you think your plant-based diet might not be in balance, you may also want to make sure you're getting enough vitamin B2 (riboflavin), B6 (pyridoxine) and selenium.

Covering the bases

B12 is the only nutrient within a vegan diet which must ordinarily be supplemented; but a number of multivitamin/mineral supplements are available for vegans to "top up" other nutrients they may be concerned about. You should only use any supplement as a safety belt, and not to make up for a poor diet: in most cases, nature is the best provider and natural foods contain many other nutrients, both known and unknown, which are beneficial for health.

What to say if your doctor challenges you on your diet

If you are eating a balanced vegan diet and paying attention to the above, there's no reason to worry about your health. In fact, the evidence available suggests you're likely to be better off than most of the developed world. So if your doctor disapproves of your diet – talk with them about any concerns they may have about your situation in particular, and show them this book (and if they don't appear to be listening - find another doctor!). There are a great many sympathetic doctors out there. In fact a growing number are vegan themselves.

BEATING DIABETES TYPE 2 WITH VEGAN FOOD

Insulin is the hormone that acts like a key to let glucose from our digested food pass out of the bloodstream into the cells of the body to be used for energy. Type 1 diabetes is a disease where the pancreas is no longer able to make insulin. It is managed with regular insulin injections. Type 2 diabetes, which is around 90% of all diabetes, is where the body cannot make good use of the insulin it does produce. High levels of natural trans fats and saturated fats in the bloodstream from eating animal products, even in a slim person, interfere with the action of insulin. The resulting raised glucose level, known as hyperglycaemia, causes long-term damage to the body and eventual failure of various organs and tissues.

The good news is that type 2 diabetes can be reversed with a wholefood plant-based diet and physical activity. Management of type 1 diabetes is also easier on a healthy vegan diet, with less insulin needing to be injected. Unfortunately many doctors, and shockingly also diabetes charities, don't yet know this, or consider a healthy vegan diet approach to be "too extreme." However, that is starting to change. With 10% of the UK National Health Service budget being spent on treating this largely preventable disease and its complications, that change cannot come too soon.

Dr Rajiv Bajekal is a Consultant Spinal Surgeon (rajivbajekal.com and instagram @drrajivbajekal) with a history of type 2 diabetes in his family. After moving to Britain and starting his own family, he started to eat a lot of convenience food high in fat, sugar and salt, such as egg, cheese or tuna sandwiches, crisps and fizzy drinks from the hospital canteen. The weight piled on. Although he cut out meat and chicken for ethical reasons and junk food, he continued to eat fish, eggs and dairy products. As well as gaining weight, his eyesight started to deteriorate, and his blood cholesterol and markers for diabetes rose. He also had recurring back pain and acid reflux. He attempted to take control of his health by going on an 800 Calorie per day diet for six weeks, and cycling over 30 miles per week. This took some of the excess weight off, though his diabetes markers still rose.

He stumbled across the documentary *Forks Over Knives* on Netflix. This was the wake-up call he needed to give up the eggs, fish and dairy. With the full support of his already ethical vegan wife Dr Nitu Bajekal, who is a lifestyle medicine physician and gynaecologist (nitubajekal. com and @drnitubajekal), he adopted a wholefood plant-based diet with no oil, and lost 17kg with very little effort. His total cholesterol fell to a healthy 3.8mmol/L (below 150mg/dL). His sleep and energy levels improved, and the back pain and acid reflux no longer troubled him. He now avoids eating after 7p.m. or before noon, and he snacks on fruit which he loved, but thought it was best to avoid for diabetics!

Dr Bajekal says: "Since my success in reversing chronic illness, I have qualified as a lifestyle medicine practitioner (at the age of 56 and having trained as an orthopaedic surgeon). I find this knowledge really helps me to examine and treat patients more holistically. For example, if I see a patient with back pain, I will look at their weight, blood pressure and other factors to help me evaluate why they are experiencing this pain. Lifestyle advice can help avoid the need for surgery. I use every opportunity to help others learn what I as a medical practitioner was unaware of."

BRITAIN'S LOWEST-PRESCRIBING DOCTOR

Back in the 20th century on a council estate in south London, family doctor **Dr David Ryde**, a county athlete and rugby player and medical adviser to the British Olympic team, noticed that vegetarians tended to be slimmer. He started to study the literature on links between diet and health and was the first doctor in Britain to offer patients the option of lifestyle changes rather than drugs and surgery. He discovered that dietary modifications could cause positive and dramatic changes in longstanding conditions including angina, obesity, arthritis, diabetes, hypertension (high blood pressure), premenstrual tension, chronic dyspepsia (indigestion) and acne, in some cases in weeks or even days. The results became even more impressive when patients cut down on animal products.

In one case published in *The Vegan* magazine in the nineties a head teacher, who had suffered a heart attack and had to take early retirement, followed Dr Ryde's suggestion to switch to a plant-based diet. His heart disease was reversed and he went on to run a marathon and take up hill walking.

Dr Ryde told us that whilst most non-smokers might live to around 80 or 90 years, the non-vegans constantly needed to visit his surgery during their last 10 or 15 years. Whereas his vegan patients were in good health almost until the end, then "went down quickly in the last few months." In his clinical experience, healthy vegan diets are not just about longevity, but also quality of life and impact on the health system.

Donald Watson, inventor of the word *vegan*, was still hillwalking in his nineties

BEATING HEART DISEASE WITH VEGAN FOOD

In America, vegan doctors have for decades achieved spectacular results using no-cost plant-based wholefood diets to reverse diabetes type 2, improve management of diabetes type 1, and also to halt the progression of heart disease and in some cases cause it to regress. They are tackling the lifestyle *causes* of disease, not just mitigating the symptoms with drugs and expensive surgery.

One of the very first was **Dr Dean Ornish**, who began treating patients with plant-based diets in 1977. At that time it was generally believed to be impossible to reverse coronary heart disease. In fact, governments believed that ordinary people were incapable of making and maintaining big lifestyle changes. Dr Ornish and his colleagues showed otherwise.

Some of their coronary heart disease patients, a control group, followed the normal programme that doctors recommend of eating lean meat and fish. A second group followed a low-fat, plant-based diet, exercising moderately, stress management techniques and group support meetings. One year later the first group had more frequent, severe and longer angina, while the second group reported a 91% reduction in the frequency of angina, 42% reduction in duration, and 28% reduction in severity. In other studies they had found similar improvements in angina after just one month. Average stenosis (blood vessel narrowing) got worse in the control group; it improved in the experimental group, and those who made the greatest lifestyle changes showed the biggest improvement. They concluded that "small changes in lifestyle may slow the progression of atherosclerosis, whereas substantial changes in lifestyle may be required to halt or reverse coronary atherosclerosis." Also "Our trial suggests that comprehensive lifestyle changes may begin to reverse coronary atherosclerosis in only a year." In 1983 their findings were published in the *Journal of the American Medical Association* and in 1990 in *The Lancet*.

In 1985 **Dr Caldwell Esselstyn**, an Olympic rowing champion and surgeon during the Vietnam war, was aware of Dean Ornish's work linking low-cholesterol and low-fat diets to cardiovascular health. He persuaded some of his heart patients to try a diet based on grains, pulses, vegetables and fruit, avoiding animal products and oil. Some of these patients had been told they had less than a year to live. However, of the 17 who stuck to his programme, during the next 12 years not one of them suffered a cardiac event. In 1997 he published the book *Prevent and Reverse Heart Disease*. While critics pointed out that his claims "are not backed up by rigorous clinical trials", it was obvious that he was on to something. His career is documented in the film *Forks Over Knives*. To quote Dr Esselstyn, "My main concern was cardiovascular disease. Other physicians are finding that isn't the only disease that is turned around by this. Diabetes, hypertension, strokes, vascular dementia, ulcerative colitis, Crohn's disease, rheumatoid arthritis, lupus, multiple sclerosis, allergies, asthma, renal disease, the list goes on. Never before in medicine have we had a tool so powerful in our toolbox."

One of the biggest vegan lifestyle programmes in America is **CHIP**, the Complete Health Improvement Program, founded by **Dr Hans Diehl**, professor of preventive medicine at Loma Linda University in California. CHIP participants are ordinary people who suffer with heart disease. Every day for three weeks they are gradually introduced to new information about the contribution of poor nutrition to cardiovascular health, and progressive lifestyle changes. They learn what to do at home with whole grains, beans, lentils, vegetables and so on. At the start of the programme some patients could barely walk from the car park to the lecture room. After just three weeks of lifestyle changes, some were walking from their *home* to the lecture.

Dr Diehl told us that participants do not necessarily realise at the start that they will be giving up many of their favourite animal-based foods, and if they did they might not attend. But by the time they figure out they are heading towards veganism, they already feel so much better that it is no longer an issue.

We know we are really starting to get somewhere when **Dr Kim Williams**, former president of the American College of Cardiology, is vegan and recommends it to his patients. Back in 2003, one of Dr Williams' patients reversed her own heart disease, including resolving her chest pain, in six weeks by following Dean Ornish's plant-based diet, exercise and meditation programme.

Dr Williams read up on Dr Ornish and studies of Seventh-day Adventists, a Christian denomination where many follow a plant-based diet. He realised that his own "healthy" diet, that included chicken and fish, was not so healthy at all, and switched to no-cholesterol protein sources like veggieburgers, soya sausages, nuts, and almond milk. Within six weeks his LDL cholesterol was down from 170 to 90.

Nowadays he tells his patients to go to the supermarket and try plant-based versions of the foods they already eat, some of which can even taste better. Not smoking, exercise and stress management training all play their part too.

"I recommend a plant-based diet," says Dr Williams, "because I know it's going to lower their blood pressure, improve their insulin sensitivity and decrease their cholesterol. Some patients are able to do it, and some are not." Other doctors in his hospital are following his example.

Dr Williams says: "There are two kinds of cardiologists: vegans and those who haven't read the data."

AVOIDING ALZHEIMER'S

It's not just the heart that can suffer catastrophic damage from years of poor nutrition and lifestyle choices. Clogged arteries in the brain can lead to a stroke or Alzheimer's disease. Exercise and a wholefood plant-based diet improve circulation by, for example, reducing blood pressure and cholesterol levels.

Doctors Dean and Ayesha Sherzai are uniquely qualified to advise on optimising and extending healthy brain functioning. Not only are they medical doctors specialising in neurology, they are also research neuroscientists and directors of the Brain Health and Alzheimer's Prevention Program at Loma Linda University Medical Center in California. The Sherzais state that 90% of Alzheimer's is not a genetic inevitability but, as they have seen in their clinic, can be delayed by 10 to 15 years by lifestyle and dietary changes. "Brain health depends on how you feed it, treat it, challenge it, and allow it to rest. For example, good blood circulation helps the sleeping brain efficiently clear the waste products that were generated whilst awake." Their recommendations include eating wholegrains and avoiding eggs and fish.

Their 2017 book *The Alzheimer's Solution: A Breakthrough Program to Prevent and Reverse the Symptoms of Cognitive Decline at Every Age* is the first comprehensive programme for preventing Alzheimer's and improving cognitive function. The book is based on the largest clinical and observational study to date. The Sherzais are on a mission to revolutionise healthcare by empowering communities to take control of their own health. Their next book *The 30-Day Alzheimer's Solution: The Definitive Food and Lifestyle Guide to Preventing Cognitive Decline*, is published March 2021. Read more at teamsherzai.com and instagram @teamsherzaimd.

Perhaps one day we'll be saying: "There are two kinds of neurologists: vegans and those who haven't read the data."

Other trailblazing American medical doctors such as **Michael Klaper, Joel Fuhrman** and **John McDougall** have also had huge success with plant-based diets, and published books and videos that are very popular and influential.

THE PLANT POWER GP

Dr Gemma Newman is one of a new generation of British pioneering vegan doctors prescribing plant-based diets to heal and prevent disease. By following her holistic health, nutrition and lifestyle advice, patients have achieved impressive results such as reversing type 2 diabetes, or reducing medication for type 1 diabetes by up to two-thirds. Other conditions that have improved include high blood pressure, eczema, psoriasis and perimenopause symptoms.

Dr Newman teaches other doctors and the general public in training programmes, podcasts and conferences about the benefits of plant-based nutrition, and appears in mainstream media such as magazines and national TV. Her illustrated book *The Plant Power Doctor: A simple prescription for a healthier you*, published January 2021, explains the health benefits of plant-based nutrition. There are chapters on heart disease, cancer, diabetes, skin health, and easy recipes for food that people really like. You can read more at gemmanewman.com.

THE PLANT-BASED GUT DOCTOR

Dr Alan Desmond is a vegan consultant gastroenterologist in Devon, south-west England. In his gut clinic he promotes a wholefood plant-based diet as a key component to restoring and maintaining good digestive health. Issues he specialises in include acid reflux, indigestion, stomach ulcers, bloating, coeliac disease, food intolerances, Inflammatory Bowel Disease (IBD), Crohn's disease, ulcerative colitis, diverticular disease, small intestinal bacterial overgrowth (SIBO) and Irritable Bowel Syndrome (IBS).

Dr Desmond gives talks and broadcasts on the internet about healthy eating for gut health. He offers a low cost online programme across six weeks that can be started at any time, where he does the science and dietitian Rose Martin and entertaining Irish vegan chefs David and Stephen Flynn take care of the food with recipes that are low FODMAP (fermentable oligo-, di-, mono-saccharides and polyols). His book *The Plant-Based Diet Revolution: 28 days to a happier gut and a healthier you*, published January 2021, explains the benefits, especially for the gut and microbiome, of eating wholefoods, dropping dairy, and replacing meat by plant-based protein sources. Find him on instagram

@dr.alandesmond and at devongutclinic.com.

10,000 BLACK VEGAN WOMEN

Tracye McQuirter, MPH, has for over 30 years been helping the African American community improve their health with vegan food. She is the founder of **10,000 Black Vegan Women**, a free programme to help women in black communities take charge of their health.

Tracye was originally inspired to go vegan in 1986, become an activist, and earn a Master's Degree in Public Health Nutrition, by a talk at her college by legendary comedian and civil rights activist Dick Gregory, who explained how fast food companies especially target black communities. She directed America's first federally funded vegan nutrition programme, and created the first free African American Vegan Starter Guide in partnership with Farm Sanctuary.

Tracye says "Eating whole, plant-based foods, along with exercising, being smoke-free, and maintaining a healthy weight, can reduce the risk of developing chronic diseases by 80 percent. And of these healthy lifestyle factors, what we eat is the most important. You cannot out-exercise an unhealthy diet. Good nutrition is key. Eating healthy vegan foods can not only help prevent chronic diseases, but can also treat or reverse heart disease, diabetes, obesity, and certain cancers. It's our best chance at living a longer, healthier, disease-free life."

She has published two best-selling books: *By Any Greens Necessary: A Revolutionary Guide for Black Women Who Want to Eat Great, Get Healthy, Lose Weight, and Look Phat* in 2010, and in 2018, with her mother Mary McQuirter who had gone vegan with her, *Ageless Vegan: The Secret To Living A Long And Healthy Plant-Based Life.* Her website byanygreensnecessary.com has step-by-step guidance to make going vegan easy, healthy, affordable and tasty.

In 2020, Tracye launched 10,000 Black Vegan Women, a free programme showing how to make vegan food affordable, convenient and delicious. The programme offers online video training in plant-based nutrition, food as it relates to social justice, animals and the environment, as well as cooking videos, meal plans, vegan recipes, grocery shopping lists, meal prep guides, all in a supportive online community. By October 2020 over 10,000 black women had already signed up.

PIONEERING PLANT-BASED DIETITIANS

A dietitian (also spelled dietician) is the gold standard of science based public health nutrition professional, typically holding a relevant science degree such as Dietetics plus supervised practice in the National Health Service to demonstrate clinical and professional competence. Dietitians assess, diagnose and treat dietary and nutritional problems, giving practical guidance on lifestyle and food choices. Whilst anyone can call themselves a nutritionist, the title of dietitian is the only food and nutrition title that is protected by law.

Brenda Davis and **Vesanto Melina** are two Canadian pioneering vegan dietitians who published the first edition of their book *Becoming Vegan* in 2000. That groundbreaking book covers vegan nutrition in great depth, assessing what people claim, and what the science actually shows. Other titles by one or both of them include *Defeating Diabetes* (2003), *Becoming Raw* (2010), *The Kick Diabetes Cookbook* (2018), *Kick Diabetes Essentials* (2019), and Brenda's latest book *Nourish: The Definitive Plant-Based Nutrition Guide for Families* (January 2021).

PCRM

In 1985 the American psychiatrist **Dr Neal Barnard** founded the **Physicians Committee for Responsible Medicine** (PCRM), promoting the health benefits of a wholefood vegan diet to other doctors, dietitians and the public to reverse a range of lifestyle diseases, especially diabetes type 2 and heart disease. PCRM now has over 12,000 medical doctor members, a staff of 70, and in 2016 opened a low-cost medical centre in Washington D.C.

Dr Barnard's 17 books include *Dr Barnard's Programme for Reversing Diabetes* (2007) and *The Reverse Diabetes Diet* (2010). He appears in the film *Super Size Me* and many others.

PCRM sells books at pcrm.org/shop. Shipping to Europe may be expensive, but you will be supporting their work.

PLANT-BASED HEALTH PROFESSIONALS UK

In 2017 **Dr Shireen Kassam**, a London based physician, founded **Plant-Based Health Professionals UK**. This community interest company provides education and advocacy on whole food plant-based nutrition for the prevention and treatment of chronic disease. Membership is open to all health professionals and the general public and most of their online resources and webinars are free to access. PBHP UK also provides evidence-based recommendations for public policy on nutrition, diet and lifestyle.

PBHP UK events and conferences around the UK have featured British, American and Irish vegan doctors and dietitians, including most of the pioneering vegan doctors above.

The Plant-Based Health Professionals UK website has colourful factsheets to view or download, including eating well, health and weight loss, pregnancy, children, lowering cancer risk, coeliac disease, type 2 diabetes, hypertension, stroke, triglycerides, menopause, how to avoid bloating from eating pulses, vitamin D, and more to come. There is a directory of vegan doctors, dentists, dietitians, nutritionists and allied health professionals, and affiliated organisations. You can watch videos of presentations from previous PBHP events, such as the 30-minute video *Diet and Diabetes*, in which Dr Gemma Newman explains with diagrams the causes and cure for diabetes.

In November 2019 Dr Shireen Kassam, together with the University of Winchester, launched the first university based, CPD-accredited course on plant-based nutrition in the UK. This is a fully online, 6-week distance learning course facilitated and taught by Dr Kassam and other plant-based experts, many of them members of PBHP UK.

READ AND WATCH ALL ABOUT IT

If you're on the receiving end of some alleged "science" from proponents of Atkins, paleo or other non-vegan diets, then **Dr Michael Greger** has the antidote. A general practitioner specialising in clinical nutrition, who also holds a degree in agriculture, Dr Greger and his research team review every one of the thousands of scientific papers published every year on nutrition. They eliminate those funded by vested interests and designed to show a particular result, drill down through the data to see if it's been interpreted correctly, and publish concise video summaries by topic on the website **nutritionfacts.org**. There are over 1,000 fun five-minute mini-lectures, each one summarising in plain English the latest cutting-edge science on an area of nutrition such as sugar or diabetes, and fully referenced.

Dr Greger's videos are like kryptonite for vegans who want to counter misleading nutrition propaganda put out by or bankrolled by the animal industries and processed food manufacturers.

Dr Greger's book *How Not To Die* has a chapter on how western animal-based diets contribute to each of 14 of the major western killer diseases. These include heart disease, high blood pressure, diabetes, liver diseases, lung diseases such as asthma, infections, brain diseases such as vascular dementia and Parkinson's and strokes, suicidal depression, and breast, prostate, digestive and blood cancers. He explains what we should be eating, as always backed by fully referenced, impartial science. You can watch on YouTube his presentation in London in 2016: *Uprooting the UK's Leading Causes of Death with Dr Michael Greger.*

You can find all the American and UK vegan doctors' and dietitians' books on websites such as amazon.co.uk or bookdepository.co.uk and order most of them from any bookshop. Some are also available as ebooks. Your doctor might be interested too.

Books about vegan nutrition also include:

Vegan Savvy: The Expert's Guide to Nutrition on a Plant-based Diet, Azmina Govindji R.D., December 2020

Books about vegan families include:

Your Complete Vegan Pregnancy, Reed Mangels R.D., 2019.

Nourish: The Definitive Plant-Based Nutrition Guide for Families, Brenda Davis R.D., December 2020.

Feeding Your Vegan Child — a practical guide to plant-based nutrition, Sandra Hood R.D., publication spring 2021.

Films about vegan food for health include:

What the Health
Forks Over Knives
The Game Changers

Disclaimer

Do not reduce or stop taking any medication except in consultation with your doctor. Suddenly stopping taking some drugs can be very dangerous. When making lifestyle changes, as Dr Ornish wrote: "Discuss it with your doctor so that the two of you can work together more effectively to help you achieve greater health and happiness."

CHAPTER 8

The Way of the Vegan

In chapter 1, we gave reasons to be vegan and listed fabulous vegan dishes from around the world.

In chapter 2, our friend Scarlet laid out the essential details of vegan nutrition.

In chapter 3, Ronny covered cooking at home.

Chapter 4 introduced the many tribes of vegans, from which you can create your own personal synthesis.

Chapter 5 covered non-food vegan products.

Chapter 6 looked at talking with family, friends and colleagues, and raising vegan children.

Chapter 7 featured vegan doctors empowering patients to heal themselves.

By now, you can see that veganism is much more than just a way of eating. It is a philosophy, a way of life.

The Vegan Prime Directive is the principle of non-interference with other species. Vegans do not believe in the enslavement of any life form for any purpose.

The Way of the Vegan
embraces truth,
respect,
love
for all life.

Veganism is good for us. It's good for animals. It's good for the planet. And it does not involve any extra cost. Why on earth shouldn't veganism take over the world? Once you know why and how, it's as obvious and do-able as freedom and votes for all.

Let's save the world, and ourselves.

VEGAN OR BUST

PLANET EARTH	
PRE-VEGAN	VEGAN
CO_2 rising	CO_2 falling
Forests felled	Forests restored
Desertification	Fertility
Food poverty	Plenty
Wars for resources	Co-operation
Planet, busted!	Planet, sorted!

PEOPLE	
PRE-VEGAN	VEGAN
In denial	In control
Clogged arteries	Clear arteries
Diabetes rampant	Diabetes rare
Flagging at fifty	Nifty at fifty
Rocky old age	Ripe old age
Apprehensive	Delighted

ANIMALS	
PRE-VEGAN	VEGAN
Slaves	Friends
Massacred	Honoured
Oceans empty	Seas teeming
Mass extinction	Biodiversity
Nature annihilated	Nature restored

FARMING	
PRE-VEGANIC	VEGANIC
Aggro-culture	Horticulture
Meat madness	Sustainability
Dairy delusion	Plant paradise
Erosion	Resilience
Mountains of shit	Composting
Filthy water	Clear water
Precarious	Profitable

ECONOMIES	
PRE-VEGAN	VEGAN
Pouring taxes into: lifestyle diseases pandemics subsidies wars	Investing in: education leisure people pensions
Bankrupt	Thriving

Evolving from the barbarism of a pre-vegan world
to the paradise of a vegan world is not a job for governments.
It's a personal decision for each of us.

CHOOSE A SIDE	
NON-VEGANS	VEGANS
Unaware of impacts of lifestyle choices	Personal self-responsibility and altruism
Indoctrination of the people by propaganda, lobbying and lies of Big Meat and Big Dairy	The truth about food production and its impacts that vegans know
Tyranny of the animal agriculture industry, owning corrupt or ignorant politicians who use our money to subsidise it, until all the trees are cut down and every sea is empty of fish	Restore nature's abundance
The risk of heart disease, diabetes, gout and preventable cancers	Vitality and mobility into old age
Humans kill everywhere, sometimes ourselves, and always others, by our non-vegan food choices	Individuals living vegan and sharing the word and the way of veganism until there are billions of us

PEOPLE MAY SAY

It's never that simple

It can be simple.

Eating vegan nowadays can be really easy, armed with this book.

Take it one meal at a time.

Turn it into an adventure, discovering new ways of eating. Seek out new foods, new veganisations. It's going to be fun trying new foods, whether ready-made treats such as vegan burgers, vegan sausages, kebabs, ice cream and chocolate, or learning how to make new dishes and desserts from scratch.

I'm at a difficult time in my life

When life is difficult and draining, coping with simple, day-to-day things like getting out of bed and cooking a meal can be a real challenge, so making positive life changes can seem too much. However, when your life seems to be spiralling out of control, one thing you can take control of is what you eat.

Eating and living vegan is about loving yourself, looking after yourself, doing the best you can for your body and our planet. The important thing is to always do your best. If you're coping with a big emotional setback, you'll have good and bad days, and won't be able to function as well as you can during happy times. As long as you're always doing your best, that's what matters. Whatever else is going on in your life, being vegan is one thing you can be consistently proud of.

I can't change the world

Whether for animals, arteries, ecology, or all of those, by being vegan you are playing your part. The food industry identifies consumer trends and responds to them. Right now, the biggest trend in food is people choosing vegan. Individually, we vegans change ourselves. As a movement, we are changing the world. This is just the beginning. The final pages of this book explain further.

If anyone questions your being vegan, whether family, friends, workmates, teachers or caterers, remember you have a basic human right to decide what you put in or on your body. Keep going and eventually they will see from your example that being vegan is a good thing. One day they might even join you. We've seen whole families go vegan.

On the other hand, if people are trying to bully you into not being vegan, if you have a problem, if no one else can help, then contact the V-Team for support. They're quite easy to find.

THE V-TEAM

You don't have to do this alone. The V-Team is the worldwide vegan movement. Millions of individuals united in thousands of local, national and international groups and organisations. Happy to help both new vegans and not-so-new vegans with any issue.

Long-established vegan charities and campaign groups include The Vegan Society, Animal Aid, Viva! (Vegetarians International Voice for Animals) and PETA (People for the Ethical Treatment of Animals).

Newer organisations with a strong online presence include Veganuary, Beyond Carnism, ProVeg, Go Vegan World, and Plant-Based Health Professionals UK.

National organisations produce great information centrally, they represent us accurately and interestingly to the media, and they help food manufacturers to make vegan versions of their products. Their staff are experienced in helping anyone, from the very young to senior citizens, reassuring parents and carers, with information by vegan nutritionists, doctors and chefs. They publish magazines, leaflets, fact sheets, websites and books.

Every year the Veganuary campaign helps hundreds of thousands of people go vegan for January. By the following August two-thirds of them have influenced by their example at least one other person to eat vegan.

If you like what these groups are doing, you can support one or more of them financially or by volunteering.

As well as the above professional vegan organisations, there are also countless amateur local, national and global Facebook vegan discussion, campaigning and social groups, probably including some covering your local area. Join in and find new vegan friends at events such as talks, walks, meals and outreach stalls.

WE ARE THE FUTURE

Having developed slowly and steadily since 1944 for seventy years until around 2015, veganism suddenly exploded across the world in just a few years. It is now the biggest trend in food, based on bulletproof science. This is only the beginning.

In the 21st century, plant-based lifestyle medicine will become the norm, with diet front and centre in healing and preventing non-infectious diseases.

Agriculture will transition from heavily subsidised, intensive, brutal, polluting and unsustainable to methods that are far better in every way, using only a quarter as much land, allowing nature to restore her forests, rivers and seas. Already we have seen struggling, depressed and desperate dairy farmers transition to growing plants for a healthy, clean profit without subsidies. And they no longer need to get up before dawn to squeeze cows' tits and shovel shit.

Vegan is the only way that nine billion people can live sustainably on this planet for the next hundred years and the thousands of years to follow.

Vegan activists will continue to use "soft power" to spread the truth about food. You might join us as a doctor, nutritionist or dietitian, vet, teacher, caterer, journalist, writer, filmmaker, politician, or study psychology and marketing to become the best advocate you can. But no pressure! Like being a non-smoker, simply by being a vegan you set an example to those around you, even if some don't initially appreciate it.

Many young people enjoy the massive satisfaction and pleasure to be had from going vegan and doing it well, at the same time recognising the unbearable consequences and pain that will continue and worsen if humans do not change our ways of living on the Earth. Older people have restored themselves to health by switching to a plant-based diet, and been rewarded with extra years and decades of pain-free, active living.

As more and more people choose the way of the vegan and teaching veganism, its growth will continue to accelerate. We can all make a difference and help our fellow citizens.

Lead by example. Be the best you can be. People follow people they think will get them where they want to be. We are what we do. Our actions define us.

How long will it take veganism to change the world? That depends on you, us, and our allies around the world. What we do, or don't do, over the next 10 or 15 years.

There is one thing stronger than all the armies of the world, and that is an idea whose time has come. That idea is veganism.

"The world belongs to those who care deeply, who dream boldy, and who work steadfastly."

Join our vegolution and let's change the world!

When all is said and done, veganism is really quite simple. Veganism is love in action.

THE VEGAN PLEDGE

DECISION TIME	
ARE YOU VEGAN?	SIGNED
Hell yeah	Alex
You bet	Ronny
...	...
...	...
...	...
...	...

Read this book and pass it along, or show it to interested friends who can get their own copy.

Let's vote with our forks, spoons and chopsticks for the lifestyle we want and the world we will leave to those who come after us.

Thank you for going vegan – have fun and good luck!

References

ENVIRONMENT

Paragraph 2: Livestock accounts for 60% of the total mass of mammals on Earth, humans 36%, and wild animals 4%. *The biomass distribution on Earth*, Yinon et al 2018, doi.org/10.1073/pnas.1711842115

Over three-quarters of all agricultural land in the world is used for animal farming. *Shifting Diets for a Sustainable Food Future.* Working Paper. Ranganathan, J et al. 2016. Washington, DC: World Resources Institute. (Modelling based on FAO source data, and factoring in both pastureland and cropland used for growing livestock feeds.)

In the UK only 15% of farmed land is used for growing food for direct human consumption, while 85% is used for grazing animals or growing feed. de Ruitera H et al. *Total global agricultural land footprint associated with UK food supply 1986–2011.* Global Environmental Change, 2017 Vol 43, pp72-81. sciencedirect.com/science/article/abs/pii/S0959378017301176

Para 3: The world's one billion cows, and billions more sheep, pigs and chickens, outnumber people by three to one. Statistics cited in *The Economist*, July 2011, based on statistics from the UN's Food and Agriculture Organisation. stage.economist.com/graphic-detail/2011/07/27/counting-chickens

Livestock production requires 45% of the world's grain. United Nations Convention to Combat Desertification, 2017. *The Global Land Outlook.* knowledge.unccd.int/glo/GLO_first_edition. (UNCCD 2017)

An estimated 90% of the world's soy is used as animal feed. Greenpeace UK, 2020. *Winging It: How the UK's chicken habit is fuelling the climate and nature emergency.* greenpeace.org.uk/resources/winging-it-chicken-soya-climate-change.

36% of the calories produced by the world's crops are used for animal feed and only 12% of those calories ultimately contribute to the human diet (as meat and other animal products). Cassidy ES et al. *Redefining agricultural yields: from tonnes to people nourished per hectare.* Environ. Res. Lett. 2013; 8 034015. iopscience.iop.org/article/10.1088/1748-9326/8/3/034015/meta

Para 4: Food animals drink more water than humans. While plant-based diets require around 1m^3 water per day, omnivorous diets require around 15m^3. UNCCD (ibid).

Intensive agriculture to grow feed crops uses millions of litres of pesticides. statista.com/statistics/662529/amount-of-agricultural-pesticide-used-uk

Para 5: More than 75% of Earth's land area is already degraded, and more than 90% could become degraded by 2050. Cherlet et al. *World Atlas of Desertification* 2018.

The UN International Organization for Migration forecasts 25 million to 1 billion environmental migrants by 2050. *Environmental Migrants: Up to 1 Billion by 2050* climateforesight.eu/migrations-inequalities/environmental-migrants-up-to-1-billion-by-2050

Para 6: Food animals are the main sources of methane and nitrous oxide. Bailey R et al, 2014. *Livestock: Climate change's forgotten sector. Global public opinion on meat and dairy consumption.* Chatham House. chathamhouse.org/2014/12/livestock-climate-changes-forgotten-sector-global-public-opinion-meat-and-dairy-consumption

Para 7: Trees cover 9% of Northern Ireland, 10% of England, 15% of Wales and 19% of Scotland. forestresearch.gov.uk, figures at 31 March 2020.

Para 8: Transport generally represents a tiny fraction of food's total emissions, at around 6% globally. Ritchie H, 2019. *Our World in Data.* ourworldindata.org/food-ghg-emissions

The main source of ocean plastic pollution is discarded gear from commercial fishing. Greenpeace, 2019. *Ghost Gear: The Abandoned Fishing Nets Haunting Our Oceans,*. greenpeace.org/international/publication/25438/ghost-gear

Para 9: Meat production requires about five times more land per unit of nutritional value than its plant-based equivalent. UNCCD (ibid).

Tree planting 'has mind-blowing potential' to tackle climate crisis. *The Guardian*, 2019. theguardian.com/environment/2019/jul/04/planting-billions-trees- best-tackle-climate-crisis-scientists-canopy-emissions

Restoring agricultural land currently used for farmed animals back to native forest would offset 12 years of current UK CO2 emissions. Harwatt, H. and Hayek, M. 2019. *Eating away at climate change with negative emissions: Repurposing UK agricultural land to meet climate goals.* pg 1 Boston: Harvard Law School. animal.law.harvard.edu/wp-content/uploads/Eating-Away-at-Climate-Change-with-Negative-Emissions%E2%80%93%E2%80%93Harwatt-Hayek.pdf

NUTRITION

Skerrett PJ and Willett WC, *Essentials of healthy eating: a guide,* Journal of Midwifery Womens Health. 55 (6). Pages 492-501, 2010.

Dewell, A, Weidner, G., Sumner, M.D, Chi, CS. and Ornish, D, 2007, *A very-Low-Fat Vegan diet Increases Intake of Protective Dietary Factors and Decreases Intake of Pathogenic Dietary Factors.* Journal of the American Dietetic Association, V108, Issue2, pp347-356.

Jacobs, DR, Tapsell, LC and Temple, NJ, *Food Synergy: The Key to Balancing the Nutrition Research Effort,* Public Health Reviews, Vol.33, No. 2, pp507-529.

Veganhealth.org/daily-needs

Department of Health, 2010, *Dietary Reference Value for Food Energy and Nutrient for the United Kingdom,* Tso.

Cramer DW, Harlow BL, Willet WC. *Galactose consumption and metabolism in relation to the risk of ovarian cancer,* Lancet. 1989;2:66-71.

WCRF Report *Diet, Nutrition, Physical Activity and Cancer: a Global Perspective,* 2018.

Vogelzangs N, Beekman AT, Milaneschi Y, Bandinelli S, Ferrucci L, Penninx BW, *Urinary cortisol and six-year risk of all-cause and cardiovascular mortality.* J Clin Endocrinol Metab. 2010;95:4959–4964.

Andrée S, Jira W, Schwind KH, Wagner H, Schwägele F, *Chemical safety of meat and meat products.* Meat Sci. 2010 Sep;86(1):38-48.

Microbiome and fibre

Long-term follow-up of the effects of fecal microbiota transplantation in combination with soluble dietary fiber as a therapeutic regimen in slow transit constipation, Zhang Y et al, 2018.

Cândido FG, Valente FX, Grześkowiak ŁM, Moreira APB, Rocha DMUP, Alfenas RCG. *Impact of dietary fat on gut microbiota and low-grade systemic inflammation: mechanisms and clinical implications on obesity,* Int J Food Sci Nutr. 2018;69(2):125-143.

Vitamin B12

Tucker K. L., Rich S., Rosenberg I., Jacques P., Dallal G., Wilson P. W. and Selhub J. *Plasma Vitamin B-12 Concentrations Relate to Intake Source in the Framingham Offspring Study.* Am J Clin Nut. 2000, Feb 71(2):514-22.

Holick MF, 2011, *Vitamin D: a delightful solution for health,* Journal of Investigative Medicine. Vol 59. Issue 6. Pages 873-880.

B12 deficiency is more common in vegans and people older than 50 years (Rauma AL 1995), but many non-vegans have a deficiency (Tucker KL et al, 2000).

Rauma, AL, Torronen, R, Hanninen, O and Mykkanen, H, 1995, *Vitamin B-12 status of long-term adherents of a strict uncooked vegan diet ("living food diet") is compromised,* The Journal of Nutrition 125:10, pp2511-2515.

Omegas

Leitzmann MF, Stampfer MJ, Michaud DS, et al, *Dietary intake of n-3 and n-6 fatty acids and the risk of prostate cancer,* Am J Clin Nutr. 2004; 80:204-16.

Yokoyama M, Origasa H, Matsuzaki M, et al. *Effects of eicosapentaenoic acid on major coronary events in hypercholesterolaemic patients (JELIS): a randomised open-label, blinded endpoint analysis.* Lancet. 2007; 369:1090-98.

Kornsteiner M, I. Singer, & I Elmadfa, *Very low n-3 long-chain polyunsaturated fatty acid status in Austrian vegetarians and vegans,* Ann Nutr Metab, 52(1):37-47, 2008.

Dairy, calcium, vitamin D

High dairy intake not associated with lower risk of osteoporis fracture: Warensjo E, Byberg L, Melhus H et al, *Dietary calcium intake and risk of fracture and osteoporosis: prospective longitudinal cohort study,* BMJ. 2011;342:d1473.

Feskanich D, Willett WC, Colditz GA. *Calcium, vitamin D, milk consumption, and hip fractures: A prospective study among postmenopausal women.* Am J Clin Nutr. 2003;77:504-511.

Chan JM, Stampfer MJ, Ma J, Gann PH, Gaziano JM, Giovannucci E. *Dairy products, calcium, and prostate cancer risk in the Physicians' Health Study,* Am J Clin Nutr. 2001;74:549-554.

Chan JM, Gann PH, Giovannucci EL. *Role of diet in prostate cancer development and progression,* J Clin Oncol. 2005;23:8152-8160.

Dairy poses increased risk of ovarian and prostate cancer: Chan JM et al, 2001; 2005; Cramer DW 1989.

Iron

Haddad EH, Berk LS, Kettering JD, Hubbard RW, Peters WR, *Dietary intake and biochemical, hematologic, and immune status of vegans compared with nonvegetarians,* Am J Clin Nutr 1999;70(suppl):586S-93S.

Hallberg L, Brune M, Rossander L, *The role of vitamin C in iron absorption,* Int J Vitam Nutr Res Suppl, 1989;30:103-8. PMID: 2507689.

Eggs and fake science

Eggs and fake science: Barnard ND et al, *Industry funding and cholesterol research: A systematic review,* Am J Lifestyle Med, Dec 2019.

Eggs are high in cholesterol and associated with increased risk of heart disease, stroke, breast cancer and prostate cancer. From nutritionfacts. org eggs section.

Ketogenic diet

Keto: Carlton J B, *Prevalence of Micronutrient Deficiency in Popular Diet Plans.* PubMed. 2010, 7:24.

Zhang Y, Zhou S, Zhou Y, Yu L, Zhang L, Wang Y. *Altered gut microbiome composition in children with refractory epilepsy after ketogenic diet.* Epilepsy Res. 2018;145:163-168.

Ye F, Li XJ, Jiang WL, Sun HB, Liu J, *Efficacy of and patient compliance with a ketogenic diet in adults with intractable epilepsy: a meta-analysis,* J Clin Neurol. 2015;11(1):26-31.

VEGAN TRIBES

Alex Bourke discussed Vegan Tribes on BBC Radio 4's *The Food Programme: Rethinking Veganism.* Listen again at bbc.co.uk/programmes/b037524t from 20 minutes.

This 25-minute broadcast also includes Donald Watson, inventor of the word *vegan*, talking about why he went vegan; a visit to a huge vegan potluck dinner in London; a meat reducer; the impossibility of feeding 9 billion people on a meat-based diet; and *Veganz* vegan supermarkets in Germany;

VEGAN DOCTORS

Can lifestyle changes reverse coronary heart disease? The Lifestyle Heart Trial. Dean Ornish, M.D. et al, The Lancet volume 336, issue 8708, pp129-133, July 21, 1990. Available at ornish.com/wp-content/uploads/can-lifestyle-changes-reverse-coronary-heart-disease.pdf

Adventist Health Study-2 (AHS-2), adventisthealthstudy.org

Index

*"Veganism is a way of living which
seeks to exclude, as far as is possible
and practicable, all forms of exploitation
of, and cruelty to, animals for food,
clothing or any other purpose."*

The Vegan Society

*"The animals of the world exist for their own reasons.
They were not made for humans any more than black people
were made for white, or women created for men."*

Alice Walker

*"I AM VEGAN. I don't eat animal products.
I don't use any animal products because of ethical,
environmental and climate reasons."*

Greta Thunberg

*"The vast majority of premature deaths can be
prevented through simple changes in diet and lifestyle."*

Michael Greger M.D., nutritionfacts.org

*"There are two kinds of cardiologists,
vegans and those who haven't read the data."*

Dr Kim Williams, cardiologist

Veganism is just love in action.

Let's vote with our forks, spoons and chopsticks
for a better world.

WE ALSO PUBLISH

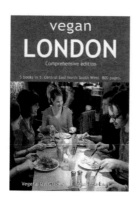

dvd

BUY NOW AT veganguides.uk

CONTRIBUTORS AND CONSULTANTS

Dean Bracher is a vegan campaigner and former staff member at The Vegan Society.

Chapter 1, Animals

Catherine Laurence BA, MSc has worked as a lawyer and environmental planner, and now spreads her time working and volunteering full time to promote the benefits of plant-based diets. She coordinated the 2013 *London Vegan Pledge*.

Chapter 1, Environment

Sandra Hood is a diabetes specialist dietitian for the National Health Service who runs education sessions for patients and health professionals. She has written a book on vegan nutrition in babies and children and is an advisor to the Vegan Society.

Chapter 2, Nutrition

CONTRIBUTORS AND CONSULTANTS

Rudy Penando co-founded *Pogo*, London's first vegan cafe, and founded its first vegan shop *VX* and the first UK vegan Merch company *Secret Society of Vegans*.

Chapter 4, Vegan Tribes

An experienced dog and cat veterinarian, **Andrew Knigh**t is Professor of Animal Welfare, and Founding Director of the Centre for Animal Welfare at the University of Winchester. He leads a masters degree in animal welfare.

Chapter 5, Vegan Pets

Chrissy Leyland holds a postgraduate diploma in Integrative Counselling, and was a co-founder of *Pogo* vegan café, *London Vegan Campaigns* and the *London Vegan Pledge*, and *The Vegan Approach*.

Chapter 6, Parenting